Interactive Student Notebook

Bring Science Alive!
Exploring Science Practices

Chief Executive Officer
Bert Bower

Chief Operating Officer
Amy Larson

Director of Product Development
Maria Favata

Strategic Product Manager
Nathan Wellborne

Senior Science Content Developer
Ariel Stein

Curriculum Consultants
Kim Merlino
Joan Westley

Program Editors
David Fraker
Mikaila Garfinkel
Edward Helderop
Rebecca Ou
Ginger Wu

Production Manager
Jodi Forrest

Operations & Software Manager
Marsha Ifurung

Designer
Sarah Osentowski

Art Direction
Julia Foug

TCi™

Teachers' Curriculum Institute
PO Box 1327
Rancho Cordova, CA 95741

Customer Service: 800-497-6138
www.teachtci.com

ISBN 978-1-58371-984-8
5 6 7 8 9 10 -DH- 23 22 21 20 19 18

Manufactured by Hess Print Solutions, Brimfield, OH
United States of America, October 2018, Job # 274281

Contents

Unit 1 Living Things and Ecosystems

Unit 2 Earth Systems

Unit 3 Changes in Matter

Unit 4 Earth, the Moon, and the Stars

What Is an Ecosystem?

Phenomenon: All sorts of different animals can meet their needs in the same area.

What questions do you have about this phenomenon?

After the lesson, use what you learned to explain this phenomenon.

1. Organisms and Their Environment

Look at this list of living and nonliving things in the ecosystem at the top of the Grand Canyon.

Living Things	Nonliving Things
snake	air
raven	water
lizard	sand
pine tree	rocks
flower	soil
bush	sunlight

What do you think are three ways living things and nonliving things interact in this ecosystem?

2. A Tropical Rainforest Ecosystem

Why do you think a rainforest ecosystem would have a much greater number and variety of plants and animals than the ecosystem at the top of the Grand Canyon?

3. A Pond Ecosystem

List three organisms that might live in a pond ecosystem. Give one reason why each organism might not survive in another ecosystem.

4. How Scientists Study Ecosystems

	Hydrologist	Hydrologists study how water moves through ecosystems. They also look at how clean water is and how different organisms in ecosystems use the water that is available.
	Botanist	Botanists study plants in the wild. They look for where different kinds of plants grow and how they get water, sunlight, and nutrients. They also look at how plant species move between ecosystems.
	Environmental Consultant	Environmental consultants look at how human activity and buildings affect ecosystems. Some of them work at dams, and they study how the dam affects the organisms that live in the river ecosystem that was dammed.
	Ecotoxicologist	Ecotoxicologists study how toxic chemicals, or poisons, affect organisms in ecosystems. They often study plants on farms to see if the plants are safe from dangerous substances.
	Animal Behaviorist	Animal behaviorists study what animals do in ecosystems. They look at how animals survive and interact with other parts of the ecosystem. Many times, they track animals in the wild to see where they move and how they live.

Read about each of these ecologists. Choose one that you might want to be when you are older. Why does that type of ecologist interest you the most?

In this Science Skill Builder, you will take on the role of an ecologist. You will visit many different types of ecosystems and record careful observations in a journal.

Follow these steps:

1) Look at the map. Choose a location that you want to explore.

2) Carefully "fly" around the room to find the placard that matches this location's letter.

3) Write the name of the ecosystem in the blank.

4) Then complete one of the journal entries for this location.

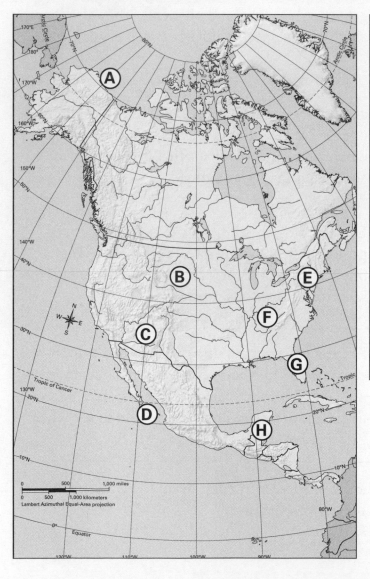

A) _____

B) _____

C) _____

D) _____

E) _____

F) _____

G) _____

H) _____

As you visit each ecosystem,

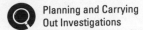
Planning and Carrying
Out Investigations

- record the name of the ecosystem on one of the journals.
- sketch one living thing and one nonliving thing you observe.
- describe two interactions between the plants, animals, and nonliving things that can occur in this ecosystem.
- write down one question an ecologist might ask to further investigate this ecosystem.

Ecosystem: _____

Sketch one living thing	Two interactions
Sketch one nonliving thing	One question

Ecosystem: _____

Sketch one living thing	Two interactions
Sketch one nonliving thing	One question

Ecosystem: _____

Sketch one living thing	Two interactions
Sketch one nonliving thing	One question

Ecosystem: _____

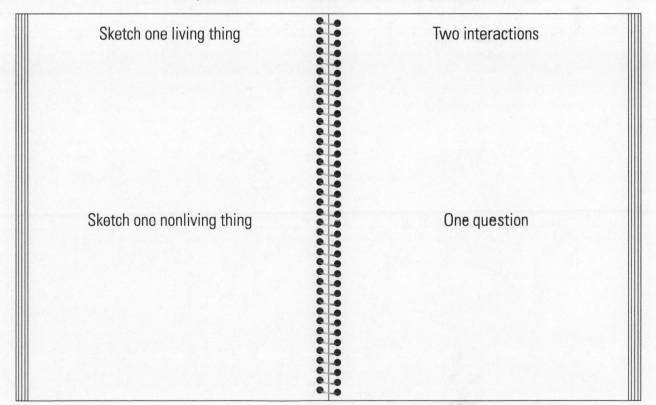

Sketch one living thing

Two interactions

Sketch one nonliving thing

One question

Ecosystem: _____

Sketch one living thing

Two interactions

Sketch ono nonliving thing

One question

Ecosystem: _____

Sketch one living thing	Two interactions
Sketch one nonliving thing	One question

Ecosystem: _____

Sketch one living thing	Two interactions
Sketch one nonliving thing	One question

Ecosystem: _____

Sketch one living thing	Two interactions
Sketch one nonliving thing	One question

Choose one of the ecosystems you learned about in this lesson. Brainstorm at least three scientific questions that could be asked and answered through further investigation of the ecosystem.

Then write a letter to an ecologist describing what you already have observed in this ecosystem and the additional questions you have. Make sure to include:

• a salutation.
• a paragraph explaining the ecosystem you traveled to and what you found there. Describe the interactions you saw among living and nonliving things.
• a paragraph with three additional questions that could be investigated.
• a closing.

What Is the Role of Producers in an Ecosystem?

Phenomenon: Plants like these bromeliads grow on tree branches instead of in the ground.

What questions do you have about this phenomenon?

After the lesson, use what you learned to explain this phenomenon.

1. Producers Make Food

Define what a **producer** is in your own words. Then give three examples of producers that you have seen in your life, and explain how you know they are producers.

2. Photosynthesis Uses Both Matter and Energy

1) Draw a line connecting the labels to their correct places on the diagram.

Chlorophyll   **Sugar**   **Water from the soil**

Oxygen   **Carbon dioxide**   **Light source**

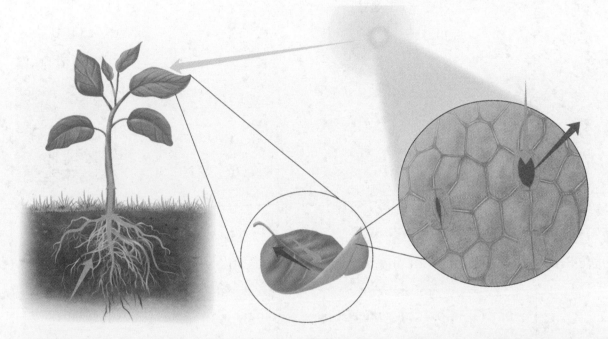

2) Write a detailed caption for your completed diagram. Include these terms in your caption: **water from the soil**, **light source**, **oxygen**, **carbon dioxide**, **chlorophyll**, and **sugar**.

3. Producers Store Excess Food

You have read that different plants store food in different parts of their bodies. Where do you think the daffodil in this picture stores its food? Why do you think that?

4. Photosynthesis Produces Wastes

You have now learned a lot about photosynthesis. Look at the word equation below.

$$\text{carbon dioxide} + \text{water} \longrightarrow \text{sugar} + \text{oxygen}$$

1) Explain where plants get carbon dioxide and water from.

2) Now explain what plants use sugar for. What about oxygen?

5. Where the Matter for Photosynthesis Comes From

Jan van Helmont could not see the carbon dioxide in the air, so he thought that all the weight his willow tree gained came from the water he added. Describe in your own words his experiment, and why Jan van Helmont came to the conclusion that he did.

5 Years

In this Response Group, you will analyze data from a hypothetical plant experiment. You will draw conclusions from the data in order to make an argument about what plants need for growth.

Question: *What does a plant really need to survive and grow?*

Control Plant

	Height (cm)	Weight (g)	Number of Leaves	Overall Appearance
Week 1	4 cm	3 g	3	Small, green, and healthy
Week 2	6 cm	8 g	5	Green, taller and healthy
Week 3	9 cm	16 g	7	Green, taller, and healthy
Week 4	13 cm	27 g	10	Green, tall, and healthy

1) Discuss each question with your group, and record your answers: Analyzing and Interpreting Data

a) What observations can you make about the growth of the control plant?

b) What do you think plants need to grow?

c) From where do you think plants get most of the matter they need to grow?

Experimental Plant A – No Water

	Height (cm)	Weight (g)	Number of Leaves	Overall Appearance
Week 1				
Week 2				
Week 3				
Week 4				

2) When the data are revealed,

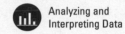
Analyzing and Interpreting Data

- copy them into the table above. Make sure to convert all the heights to centimeters and all the weights to grams.
- discuss what conclusions you can draw from the data. Write them below.

Experimental Plant B – No Soil

	Height (cm)	Weight (g)	Number of Leaves	Overall Appearance
Week 1				
Week 2				
Week 3				
Week 4				

3) When the data are revealed,

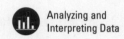 Analyzing and Interpreting Data

- copy them into the table above. Make sure to convert all the heights to centimeters and all the weights to grams.
- discuss what conclusions you can draw from the data. Write them below.

Experimental Plant C – No Light

	Height (cm)	Weight (g)	Number of Leaves	Overall Appearance
Week 1				
Week 2				
Week 3				
Week 4				

4) When the data are revealed,

 Analyzing and Interpreting Data

- copy them into the table above. Make sure to convert all the heights to centimeters and all the weights to grams.
- discuss what conclusions you can draw from the data. Write them below.

Experimental Plant D – No Carbon Dioxide

	Height (cm)	Weight (g)	Number of Leaves	Overall Appearance
Week 1				
Week 2				
Week 3				
Week 4				

5) When the data are revealed,

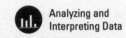 Analyzing and Interpreting Data

- copy them into the table above. Make sure to convert all the heights to centimeters and all the weights to grams.

- discuss what conclusions you can draw from the data. Write them below.

6) Complete the claim below. Then provide at least two pieces of evidence that support the claim.

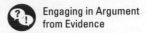 Engaging in Argument from Evidence

Question: *What does a plant really need to survive and grow?*

Claim: Plants get the materials they need for growth mainly from

_____and _____.

Evidence:

Evidence #1: Plants need _____.
I know this because…

> Hint #1: Find a set of data that showed one thing plants must have to grow.

Evidence #2: Plants do not need _____.
I know this because…

> Hint #2: Find a set of data that showed one thing plants do not have to have to grow.

Imagine you are a plant! Complete each of the statements, in order, on this diagram.

A) Caption: "Most plants are _____ .
   That means we make our own _____ !
   I use a process called _____ to do this."

B) "I get my energy from the _____ ."

C) "I get one of the materials I need from the air, a gas called _____ ."

D) "The matter I am made of comes mostly from air and _____ ,
   not from the soil."

E) "For food, I produce _____ . I also release a waste product called
   _____ that is very important to humans."

What Is the Role of Consumers in an Ecosystem?

Phenomenon: Pigs grow larger as they eat.

What questions do you have about this phenomenon?

After the lesson, use what you learned to explain this phenomenon.

1. Consumers Eat Other Organisms

Define what a **consumer** is in your own words. Then give three examples of consumers that you have seen in your life, and explain why you think they are consumers.

2. Digestion Breaks Down Food to Release Energy

1) Draw a line connecting each label to its correct place on the diagram.

Stomach

Small intestine

Mouth

Large intestine

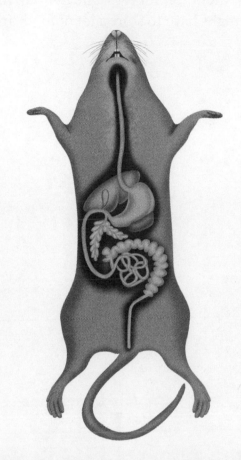

2) Write a detailed caption for your completed diagram. Include these terms in your caption: **digestive system**, **digestive juices**, **energy**, and **building materials**.

3. Consumers Store Excess Food

You have learned that birds need to gain a lot of weight before they migrate long distances, because many of them cannot eat while they are migrating. What do you think is another consumer that might have to store a lot of food, and why?

4. Consumers Produce Wastes

Explain three different ways most consumers produce wastes. Where do the wastes go after they are produced?

5. Humans Are Consumers

You have learned that humans, like all consumers, have needs that must be met if they are to survive. What are some needs that must be met for you to survive? Describe at least three.

In this Small Group Investigation, you will dissect an owl pellet to identify what owls eat. Then you will create a diagram that models how the energy in owls' food was once energy from the sun.

1) Draw and label each of the remains you find in your owl pellet. Use the owl reference poster to help you identify each one. (If you cannot identify the remains, you can research online or label the remains with a question mark.)

Planning and Carrying Out Investigations

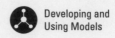
Developing and
Using Models

2) Create a diagram that models the flow of energy from the sun
to the owl.

- Below the owl, draw each of the organisms your class discovered that owls eat.
  Draw arrows to show energy flowing from the organisms to the owl.
- Then research what plants and animals are eaten by the organisms the owl eats.
  Add those to your diagram. Draw arrows to show the transfer of energy.
- Draw arrows from the sun to any producers in your diagram.

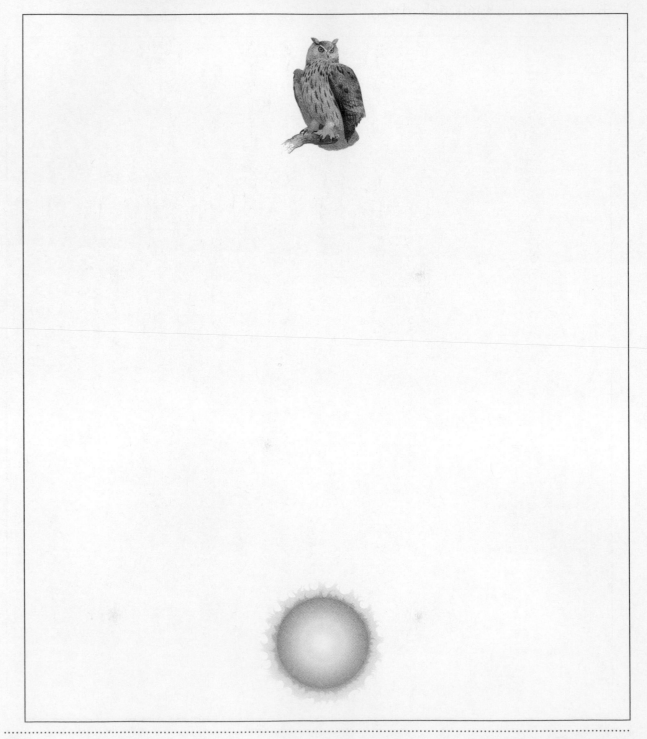

3) Complete the claim below. Then draw a diagram that you can use as evidence to support the claim. Finally, explain how your diagram supports the claim.

Constructing Explanations and Designing Solutions

Claim: All energy that humans use was once energy from the _____.

Evidence:

Hint: In your diagram, include a human, the sun, at least one producer, and at least one other consumer.

Reasoning:

Hint: Explain how your diagram supports the claim. Make sure to talk about energy transfer.

The flowchart below models how energy flows throughout an ecosystem. Follow the directions next to each box to complete the model.

Draw yourself. Then complete the caption.

I get the energy I need to live and grow from…

_____

_____ .

Draw a consumer that a human might eat. Complete the caption.

This consumer got its energy by…

_____

_____

_____ .

Draw a producer that might be eaten by the consumer above. Complete the caption.

Producers get their energy by…

_____

_____

_____ .

Draw the most likely **source of energy** for the producer above. Complete the caption.

Almost all of an ecosystem's energy comes from…

_____ .

What Is the Role of Decomposers in an Ecosystem?

Phenomenon: People save food wastes for compost piles.

What questions do you have about this phenomenon?

After the lesson, use what you learned to explain this phenomenon.

1. Some Organisms Are Decomposers

Define what a **decomposer** is in your own words. Then give three examples of decomposers that you have seen in your life, and explain why you think they are decomposers.

2. Decomposers Recycle Matter

You have just learned how decomposers can break down dead material from organisms and turn it into soil. Draw a picture of this process happening for some sort of dead material. It can be a material that naturally occus in the forest, food scraps you produced, or something else. Write a description of what is being shown in your drawing.

3. Some Decomposers Can Store Excess Food

You have learned that some decomposers, like mushrooms and other fungi, can store food as sugar. What does the stored food do for them?

4. Decomposers Produce Wastes

Look at this picture. When decomposers start to break down those apples on the ground, how will their wastes help the apple trees?

5. Humans Can Help to Decompose Wastes

Even though you are not a decomposer, you can help decomposers work by building compost piles. Explain in your own words what compost is, and what sorts of things you can add to it.

In this Small Group Investigation, you will explore what happens when sugar and yeast (a decomposer) are mixed together in water. Then you will carry out an investigation and make observations to produce evidence for your answer.

1) Record the question you are trying to answer in this investigation.

Planning and Carrying Out Investigations

2) How will you investigate this question? Use **controlled**, **trial**, and **variable** in your answer.

Planning and Carrying Out Investigations

3) Draw a diagram of the three bottles at the beginning of the investigation. Label what is in each bottle.

Planning and Carrying Out Investigations

4) Draw a diagram of each of the three bottles after 24 hours. Label what is in each one.

Planning and Carrying Out Investigations

5) Describe any changes you observed between the bottles before and after leaving them for a day.

Developing and Using Models

6) Explain why the bottle with the yeast and sugar had an inflated balloon, but the other two bottles did not.

Constructing Explanations and Designing Solutions

Decomposers are nature's recyclers. Draw a diagram of a compost pile at three points in time—the beginning, two months later, one year later. Assume that no new materials are added to your pile. Include in the diagram: decomposers, soil, and dead matter for the decomposers to break down. Label these parts.

Give your diagram a title that explains why decomposers are so important to ecosystems.

How Do Matter and Energy Move in an Ecosystem?

Phenomenon: Some animals only eat animals. Some animals only eat plants.

What questions do you have about this phenomenon?

After the lesson, use what you learned to explain this phenomenon.

1. Matter Remains in an Ecosystem

Looking at the diagram, describe in your own words how carbon and oxygen move through an ecosystem.

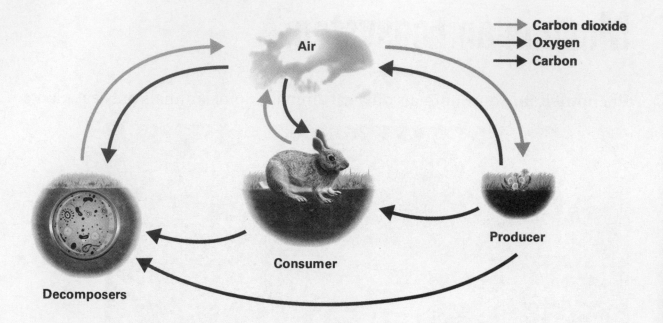

2. Energy Is Lost from an Ecosystem

Looking at the diagram, describe how energy moves through an ecosystem. Remember to explain why energy is not cycled through an ecosystem like matter is.

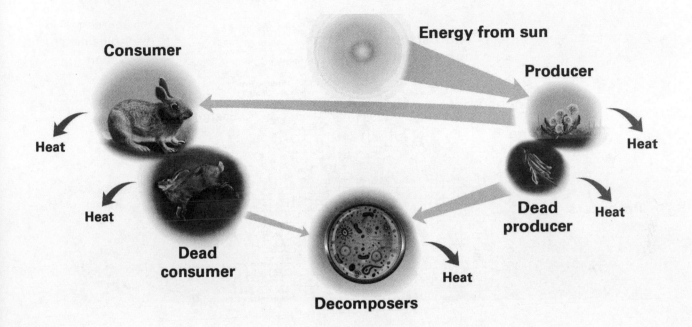

3. Energy Flows Through Food Chains

Create a caption for this diagram. Include these terms: **energy pyramid**, **food chain**, **energy**, **energy loss**, **consumer**, and **producer**.

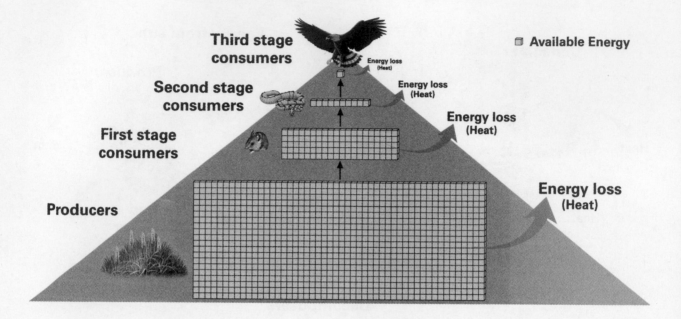

4. Many Organisms Make Up a Food Web

Look at this food web. What does a food web tell you about the organisms in an ecosystem? What do the arrows in a food web show?

Consumers

Producers

5. Humans Are Parts of Food Chains and Food Webs

Draw a food web that has you in it. Think about the different foods you eat and where those come from. Remember that might include chickens, cows, beans, tomatoes, apples, or anything else you might eat! Include at least six different pieces in your food web.

In this Whole Class Investigation, you will develop a model of a food chain and a food web using pictures of plants and animals. Then you will describe how matter and energy move through these models.

1) Create a diagram of your food chain. Include the sun and names of the organisms. Draw yellow arrows to show how energy moves through the food chain.

Developing and Using Models

2) Draw black arrows in the diagram above to show how matter moves through your food chain. Then describe how matter moves through the food chain.

Analyzing and Interpreting Data

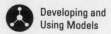
Developing and
Using Models

3) Create a diagram for your class's food web. First, include the sun and the names of the organisms in the food chain. Then, draw yellow arrows to show how energy moves through the food web. Finally, draw black arrows to show how matter moves through the food web.

4) Use your class's food web to describe one path matter can take in a tropical rainforest ecosystem.

Draw a simple picture of one of these ecosystems: ocean, pond, desert, or urban city. Your picture should include:

- a producer, a first stage consumer, and a second stage consumer.
- black arrows to show how matter is recycled in the ecosystem.

Describe how matter moves in the ecosystem you selected. Use these terms in your answer: **air**, **consumer**, **decomposer**, **producer**, **soil**, and **water**.

What Makes an Ecosystem Healthy or Unhealthy?

Phenomenon: The wintercreeper plant has taken over this area and toppled some trees.

What questions do you have about this phenomenon?

After the lesson, use what you learned to explain this phenomenon.

In this Response Group, you will engage in a debate about what actions should have been taken with the Yellowstone ecosystem at various points in its history.

1) Read the text below. Then decide which option you would choose.

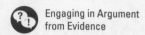 Engaging in Argument from Evidence

---

Yellowstone in 1872

Yellowstone National Park has just been founded in 1872. The western United States is still a vast wilderness. With hardly any settlers in the area near the park yet, the land outside of it still doesn't look all that different from what is inside the boundaries.

Life is hard here, and the vast wild lands are intimidating and dangerous. People raise cattle and try to survive the harsh winters. But in the long dark of winter and in the middle of the night, large packs of wolves descend from the mountains to kill cattle and sheep. Ranchers frequently find their prized animals injured or killed. Sometimes, wolves attack livestock but don't even eat the animal, leaving it to rot on the ground.

Suppose you were a rancher trying to survive in this harsh land. Most of your neighbors shoot any wolf they see on sight. But many ranchers also want help from the government to get rid of the wolves for good. *What would you do? Why?*

Options

A) Spend years building a fence around your whole property.

B) Try to convince the government to pay for lost cattle and sheep, but leave the wolves alone.

C) Kill only the wolves that come on your property or attack your cattle.

D) Ask the government to kill all the wolves in the Yellowstone area to deal with the problem for good.

2) Read the text below. Then decide which option you would choose.

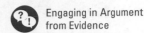 Engaging in Argument from Evidence

---

Yellowstone in 1935

Wolves have been eliminated from the American West. Yellowstone National Park and the area around it are now free of wolves.

Without wolves in the area, elk populations have been increasing quickly. The large numbers of elk have been eating a lot more plants than they used to. When wolves were regulating the numbers of elk at a lower, natural level, the plants had time to grow back before they were browsed again. But now the elk are eating them faster than they can grow back.

In some places, the vegetation is getting pretty thin. Plants in many areas are being completely killed, leaving only bare soil behind. Without plants to hold the soil, erosion is polluting trout streams. With fewer plants left to eat, the elk themselves are not as healthy as they used to be.

Suppose you were a park manager. Park visitors like to see the large numbers of elk. People outside the park like to hunt the elk when the elk wander over the park border. In general, most people are not yet aware of the problems that having too many wild plant-eaters can cause. *What would you do? Why?*

Options

A) Do nothing extra. Having lots of elk is great.

B) Hunt the elk to bring their numbers back down.

C) Bring some wolves back to the area to control the elk.

D) Bring new, foreign types of plants and animals into Yellowstone to see if that fixes things.

3) Read the text below. Then decide which option you would choose.

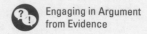 Engaging in Argument from Evidence

Yellowstone in 1995

Problems with the elk have continued and gotten worse. There are so many elk that several species of trees cannot even reproduce anymore. And it's not just the aspen trees. Most young willows and cottonwoods along streams have been eaten down to the ground. These plants used to provide cover and nesting areas for songbirds and other animals. The trees also used to be the food of beavers. The beavers built dams and made ponds that ducks and many other species lived in. Now that the elk have killed most of the young trees, beavers and their ponds have almost completely disappeared. The whole ecosystem has changed. Even the elk are victims of their own success. They have much less food than they used to, and in many ways life is harder. They are more at risk of disease and of starving to death in the winter.

Many ecologists and some groups of citizens have proposed bringing back wolves to the area to restore the ecosystem's balance, but many other groups disagree with this idea. Park visitors have gotten used to seeing the huge numbers of elk. The area surrounding the park has many ranches with people who work hard to make a living and are worried about wolves eating their cattle again. Most of these people like elk and hate wolves. They know that if wolves are brought back, some will leave the park and come to their ranches. To them, reintroducing wolves would be bringing back their age-old enemies.

Suppose you are an ecologist. *What would you do? Why?*

Options

A) Don't do anything. Leave the elk alone!

B) Try to convince the government to let park rangers kill more elk.

C) Reintroduce wolves, but pay ranchers for losses they suffer if wolves eat their livestock.

D) Reintroduce wolves and let everyone deal with it!

4) Read the text below. Then decide which option you would choose.

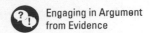

Engaging in Argument from Evidence

Yellowstone in 2009

Wolves were reintroduced to the park about 15 years ago. Environmentalists and scientists consider the reintroduction a clear success with big benefits to Yellowstone's ecosystem. Elk and coyote numbers are down to sustainable levels. Smaller animals like rabbits, owls, and foxes are more common again. Young trees have started growing. Beavers are back too. There are already ten times as many beavers as there were before the wolves returned. Scientists studying the ecosystem have gained great insights into how ecosystems work. Wolves, they have discovered, are a key species holding this ecosystem together.

But with so much food available, the wolf population has been growing quickly. Wolves have moved outside the boundaries of Yellowstone National Park, and some are killing cattle. Some people think the wolves have even been too effective at controlling elk, leaving too few elk for human hunters. Wolves keep expanding their territories farther into the Rocky Mountains with no signs of slowing down or stopping. Some people, including many ecologists who worked to reintroduce wolves, have proposed allowing limited hunting to help control the quickly-growing wolf population. But since wolves are listed as "endangered" on the endangered species list, hunting them is illegal. And many animal rights groups and some environmentalists are completely against any hunting.

Suppose you work for the federal government. You want to maintain healthy ecosystems, but also to protect people and their property. **What would you do? Why?**

Options

A) Keep wolves listed as "endangered." They are too important to kill.

B) Take wolves off the list only in states where there is a strong wolf population.

C) Remove wolves from the endangered species list nationwide.

D) Kill all the wolves again, and go back to how things were before.

1. Healthy Ecosystems

Explain in your own words why predator and prey relationships are important in healthy ecosystems. Use the following terms in your answer: **predator**, **prey**, **balance**, and **ecosystem**.

2. A Healthy Forest Ecosystem on Isle Royale

Observing predator and prey
relationships in nature can be very
difficult for scientists. What conditions
on Isle Royale might have made it easier
than in other ecosystems?

3. Unhealthy Ecosystems

```
algae  ———→  fish  ———→  turtle  ———→  heron
```

1) Look at the food chain above. What do you think would happen to the **fish** if a lot of algae grew all of a sudden and then died? Why?

2) Look at the food chain above. What do you think would happen to the **turtles** if a lot of algae grew all of a sudden and then died? Why?

3) Look at the food chain above. What do you think would happen to the **herons** if a lot of algae grew all of a sudden and then died? Why?

4. An Unhealthy Forest Ecosystem on Isle Royale

Explain in your own words how warm summers and cold winters can affect the ecosystem health of Isle Royale. Use the following terms in your answer: **wolf**, **moose**, **ticks**, **disease**, and **starve**.

In the first box, draw and label a picture of a healthy ecosystem. Include at least three different plants and animals that might be in the ecosystem.

In the second box, draw and label a picture of an unhealthy ecosystem. Include at least three different plants and animals.

Then explain how you can tell the difference between the two ecosystems.

Healthy Ecosystem

Unhealthy Ecosystem

Explanation:

How Do Ecosystems Change?

Phenomenon: Wildebeest migrate to find rainier plains.

What questions do you have about this phenomenon?

After the lesson, use what you learned to explain this phenomenon.

1. Ecosystems Can Change

Choose one of these ecosystem changes: a **flood**, a **dust storm**, a **volcano**, or a **forest fire**. Write about how you think it changes ecosystems.

2. Disturbance Leads to Succession

Succession

Describe how forest ecosystem succession happens after a disturbance like a forest fire.
Use the following terms in your answer: **pioneer**, **organism**, **trees**, and **forest fire**.

3. Changes with the Seasons

Think of an ecosystem near your home. Maybe it is a forest, or a park. Maybe it is a pond or even a garden. What does it look like during the different seasons? Draw four pictures below showing that ecosystem during winter, spring, summer, and fall.

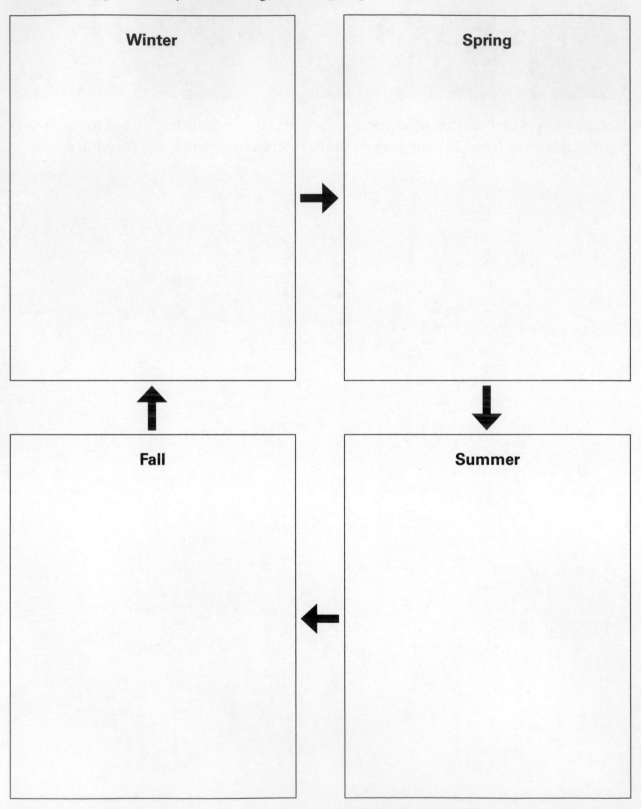

Winter

Spring

Fall

Summer

4. Climate Change and Ecosystems

Describe what happens to many ecosystems when the climate begins to warm. Use the following terms in your answer: **animal**, **plant**, **colder**, **north**, and **elevation**.

In this Visual Discovery, you will watch several silent videos depicting how ecosystems respond to change. You'll read additional text to learn more about the video. Then you will research one example in more depth and create a multimedia presentation about what you learned.

1) Circle your assigned topic:

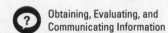 Obtaining, Evaluating, and Communicating Information

    logging   bird migration

    landslide   glacial retreat

2) With your partner, research how your assigned topic affects the components of an ecosystem and the interactions between those components. Find at least one print and one online source. List them here.

Obtaining, Evaluating, and Communicating Information

3) Discuss these questions with your partner:

Obtaining, Evaluating, and Communicating Information

- What information will you include from the Student Text and the text on the handout?

- What information will you include from your additional print and online sources?

- In what format will you create your presentation? (PowerPoint, video, narrated slideshow, posters, etc.)

- What visuals or sounds will you include to enhance your presentation?

- What tables, diagrams, or charts will you use to better communicate your main ideas?

4) Use this space to plan your multimedia presentation. You
   may wish to write a script, draw examples of visuals that you
   will include, make an outline of your presentation, etc.

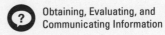

Obtaining, Evaluating, and
Communicating Information

5) Create your multimedia presentation. Prepare to share it with
   the class!

Obtaining, Evaluating, and
Communicating Information

Ecosystems can change in many ways. Some changes are slow, such as climate change, and some are fast, such as a landslide. Some changes are natural, such as bird migration, and some are caused by humans, such as logging.

Think of one thing that can cause an ecosystem to change. Then complete the boxes below by drawing a picture of the ecosystem before and after the change. In the caption box, write a paragraph explaining how and why the ecosystem changed.

Before

After

Caption:

How Do Humans Change Ecosystems?

Phenomenon: Fish have trouble surviving in polluted rivers.

What questions do you have about this phenomenon?

After the lesson, use what you learned to explain this phenomenon.

1. Humans Can Change Ecosystems

Choose one of these human causes of ecosystem change: **agriculture**, an **oil spill**, a **wildlife refuge**, or a **dam**. Write about how you think that human activity affects ecosystems.

2. Human Development and Ecosystems

Imagine you have to build homes next to this river. If you need to change this river ecosystem, what are two ways humans can do that? Which way would you choose, and why?

3. Taking Resources from Ecosystems

Humans occasionally cause damage
to coral reef ecosystems. Explain what
actions humans do to damage those
ecosystems and how they can be restored.

4. Introducing Species to Ecosystems

Choose **one** of the two invasive species below. Describe in your own words how it harms its new ecosystem.

Kudzu Vines

Zebra Mussels

In this Small Group Investigation, you will act like engineers to design a soilless farming system with a group. Then you will work with your group to build the system, observe the results, and think of ways to improve the design.

1) Define the problem your group is trying to solve. What are your criteria for a successful soilless farming system, and what are your constraints?

(?) Asking Questions and Defining Problems

Criteria:

Constraints:

2) Draw a diagram of your group's design. Label the materials, explain the purpose of each material, and describe how the seeds will get the energy and matter they need to grow.

Constructing Explanations and Designing Solutions

3) Observe your soilless farming system every other day for several weeks. Record your observations in the table below.

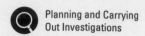

Planning and Carrying
Out Investigations

Date	Measurement	Observations

4) After your seeds have had several weeks to grow, think about how successful your solution was. Did it successfully meet your criteria and constraints? If not, what went wrong?

Analyzing and Interpreting Data

5) What are some ways you can improve your design? For example, you can consider ways you can waste less water or grow more seeds.

Planning and Carrying Out Investigations

Find three changes people have made to the ecosystem in this image.
Label them A, B, and C.

For each change that you labeled, describe the change and explain how it affects the flow
of matter in the ecosystem.

A)

B)

C)

What Are Earth's Four Systems?

Phenomenon: Lakes drain during years of low rain.

What questions do you have about this phenomenon?

After the lesson, use what you learned to explain this phenomenon.

1. Earth Has Four Systems

1) Label the four different Earth systems.

2) Write a brief explanation of what you are labeling and why whatever you have selected is part of the system. Include these terms: **atmosphere**, **biosphere**, **hydrosphere**, and **geosphere**.

2. The Atmosphere

The atmosphere contains the air you breathe and helps to keep you warm. What would happen if Earth did not have an atmosphere?

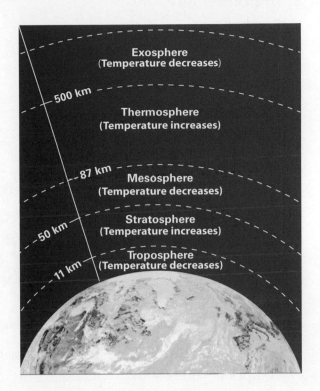

Exosphere
(Temperature decreases)

500 km

Thermosphere
(Temperature increases)

87 km

Mesosphere
(Temperature decreases)

50 km

Stratosphere
(Temperature increases)

11 km

Troposphere
(Temperature decreases)

3. The Biosphere

1) List the different Earth systems you can see in this image. Be specific, and give examples to support your claim.

2) Describe the impact that the beaver that built this dam has on at least two other Earth systems. Include two of these terms: **atmosphere**, **biosphere**, **hydrosphere**, and **geosphere**.

4. The Hydrosphere

Read the information in the box, and follow the directions.

> 97/100 of Earth's water is salt water in the ocean.
>
> The other 3/100 is fresh water.
>
> Most of the fresh water on Earth, 69/100, is frozen in glaciers.
>
> Of Earth's fresh water, 30/100 is underground.
>
> The remaining 1/100 of Earth's fresh water flows freely on the surface.

Look at the graph below. Write in the number of liters out of 100 for each bar. Use these numbers:

- 97
- 2.07
- 0.90
- 0.03

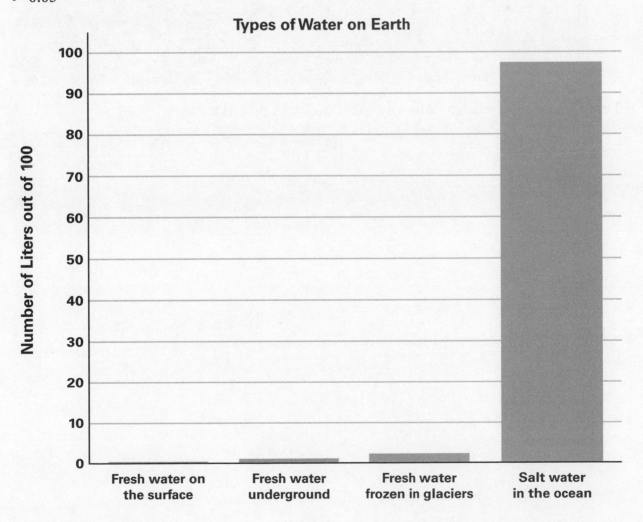

Types of Water on Earth

5. Earth's Water Cycle

1) Using the image below, draw and label the water cycle. Include these terms: **evaporation**, **condensation**, **precipitation**, **runoff**, and **water vapor**.

2) Using the water cycle, explain why water on Earth is conserved.

6. The Geosphere

1) List the different Earth systems you can see in this image. Be specific, and give examples to support your claim.

2) This image shows sedimentary rock. Sedimentary rock is formed by sediments pressed together over millions of years. What are sediments, and how can you tell that this rock is made from them?

7. Soil

Different environments on Earth have different types of soil. Write a brief sentence explaining how the soil got that way.

Environment	Soil Type	How Soil Got This Way
	Forest soil has a lot of humus, or decayed plant and animal matter.	
	Desert soil has a lot of minerals but little humus.	
	Soil in mountains is very rocky.	

In this Whole Class Investigation, you will develop an understanding of how to categorize things into Earth's four systems. Then you will build a clay model of Earth, showing each of Earth's systems. You will also graph how much water on Earth is available as drinking water.

1) Describe what kinds of things belong to each of Earth's systems.

Developing and Using Models

Geosphere	Hydrosphere
Biosphere	**Atmosphere**

2) Draw a diagram of your Earth model. Label Earth's four systems. Then find three places on your diagram where two different systems meet. Explain what might happen when these systems interact.

Developing and Using Models

3) Think of something on Earth that may belong to more than one system. Which systems might it be a part of? Explain your answer.

Asking Questions and Defining Problems

4) Record how many times thumbs covered water or land.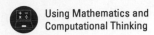

Then complete the table and color in the graph:
- How many times was water covered? Color in this many squares blue.
- How many times was land covered? Color in this many squares brown.

	Number of Times Covered by Thumb	Graph Color
Water		
Land		

Water and Land on Earth's Surface

5) There are 1,400 billion cubic kilometers of water on Earth. How many cubic kilometers do you think we can drink? Using Mathematics and Computational Thinking

Prediction: *I think we can drink _____ billion cubic kilometers out of 1,400 billion cubic kilometers of water on Earth.*

6) Record the amount of salt and fresh water on Earth.

Using Mathematics and Computational Thinking

Then complete the table and color in the graph:

- What fraction of water is salt water? Color in this many squares green.
- What fraction of water is fresh water? Color in this many squares purple.

	Fraction	**Graph Color**
Salt Water		
Fresh Water		

Salt and Fresh Water on Earth

7) Record the amount of freshwater on Earth.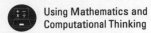

Then complete the chart and color in the graph:

- What fraction of fresh water is frozen? Color in this many squares light purple.
- What fraction of fresh water is ground water? Color in this many squares red.
- What fraction of fresh water is surface water? Color in this many squares blue.

	Fraction	Graph Color
Frozen Water		
Ground Water		
Surface Water		

Freshwater Sources on Earth

Draw a picture of what you see outside.

- Label things in your picture that are part of the atmosphere, biosphere, geosphere, and hydrosphere.
- Identify two places in your picture where two of Earth's systems interact. Describe how the systems are interacting.

How Do Earth's Systems Produce Weather and Climate?

Phenomenon: The fog in this valley stays low to the ground.

What questions do you have about this phenomenon?

After the lesson, use what you learned to explain this phenomenon.

1. Earth's Systems Interact

1) Write a paragraph describing the weather today. Which Earth systems are interacting?

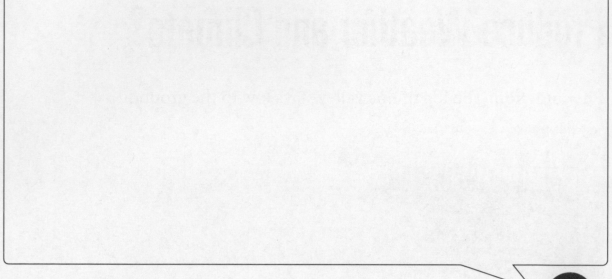

2) Write a paragraph describing the climate of the area you live in. Can you think of any reasons that your climate is like this?

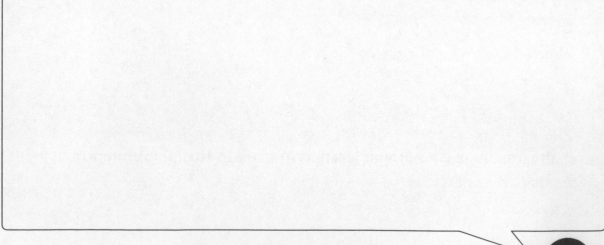

© Teachers' Curriculum Institute

2. Air Pressure and Temperature

1) What is it called when a moving warm air mass moves into a stationary cold air mass?

2) Draw a diagram showing what happens when a moving warm air mass moves into a stationary cold air mass.

3) Write a sentence explaining your diagram.

4) Cold air does not hold water vapor very well. What predictions can you make about the weather as the warm air mass moves in?

3. Clouds and Precipitation

1) Observe the clouds in your area. Draw a picture of what they look like.

2) What predictions can you make about the weather from what the clouds look like?

3) What predictions about precipitation can you make from the temperature of your area?

4) Which Earth systems interact to produce clouds and precipitation?

4. Ocean Currents

1) Which Earth system does the ocean interact with to form surface currents?

2) How does the ocean form deep water currents?

3) How do ocean currents affect climates?

4) How do ocean currents affect the fish in the biosphere?

5. Prevailing Winds

1) Draw arrows and label them to show how a breeze can form. Include these terms: **warm air** and **cool air**.

2) Draw and label how jet streams and prevailing winds can carry clouds and air masses.

In this Science Skill Builder, you will examine placards about weather and climate with a partner. For each example of weather or climate, you will determine which of Earth's systems interact to produce it. Then you will create a diagram and give a weather report about one of the examples.

1) Analyze the information at each station and complete the table.

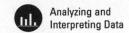 Analyzing and Interpreting Data

Which of Earth's systems . . .	Circle systems that interact.	Describe how the systems interact. Use the names of the systems.
. . . cause clouds to form over mountains?	atmosphere biosphere geosphere hydrosphere	
. . . produce hailstones?	atmosphere biosphere geosphere hydrosphere	
. . . cause the temperature to rise in a crowd?	atmosphere biosphere geosphere hydrosphere	
. . . produce fog in the morning?	atmosphere biosphere geosphere hydrosphere	

Which of Earth's systems . . .	Circle systems that interact.	Describe how the systems interact. Use the names of the systems.
. . . help warm up southern England?	atmosphere biosphere geosphere hydrosphere	
. . . help cool down northern Chile?	atmosphere biosphere geosphere hydrosphere	
. . . produce wind on beaches?	atmosphere biosphere geosphere hydrosphere	
. . . help bring snow to Florida during the winter?	atmosphere biosphere geosphere hydrosphere	

2) Your teacher assigned you a type of weather or climate. Create a diagram that shows how Earth's systems interact to produce the weather or climate. Make sure to:

Developing and Using Models

- title the diagram.
- label Earth's systems that interact to produce the weather or climate.

3) Describe how Earth's systems interact to produce the type of weather or climate in your diagram.

Engaging in Argument from Evidence

4) What happens when the geosphere, hydrosphere, or biosphere interact with the atmosphere? Use the examples you examined to support your answer.

Obtaining, Evaluating, and Communicating Info

Record observations of what the weather is like where you are.
Fill in the information below.

Location: _____ Date: _____

Temperature: _____

Precipitation: _____

Weather description: _____

_____

Complete the paragraph below to explain how two of Earth's systems interact to produce
the weather where you are.

The weather where I am is _____

Two of Earth's systems that interact to produce this weather are _____

_____

These systems work together to produce the weather by_____

_____

_____

_____

_____

_____

_____

_____

How Do Earth's Systems Change Earth's Surface?

Phenomenon: These rocks are oddly shaped.

What questions do you have about this phenomenon?

After the lesson, use what you learned to explain this phenomenon.

In this Visual Discovery, you will work in groups of four and analyze one example of how Earth's surface changed. You will create an act-it-out to model how Earth's systems interacted to cause this change.

1) In the squares below, describe how each of Earth's systems is involved with producing the change you were assigned. If the system does not affect the change to Earth's surface, you can leave the square blank.

Obtaining, Evaluating, and Communicating Info

Atmosphere	**Biosphere**
Hydrosphere	**Geosphere**

2) Write an explanation of how the systems interact to produce the change in Earth's surface you were assigned.

Constructing Explanations and Designing Solutions

3) Write a script for an act-it-out that describes and models
how Earth's systems interact to produce the change to Earth's
surface that you were assigned.

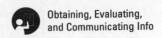 Obtaining, Evaluating,
and Communicating Info

- Make sure everyone in your group plays one of Earth's four systems.
- Every system should describe its role in your change to Earth's surface. If the
system does not help produce the change, say so in the script. If the system does
help produce the change, explain how.

4) As each group presents their skit, fill out the table. Briefly describe what role each Earth system has in producing the change to Earth's surface. If the system does not play a role in producing the change, write, "n/a."

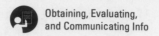

Obtaining, Evaluating, and Communicating Info

Change to Earth's Surface	Atmosphere	Biosphere	Geosphere	Hydrosphere				
Barrier Islands								
Continental Islands								
Coral Islands								
River Delta								
Rock Formations								
Sea Caves								
Soil								
Volcanic Islands								

1. Earth's Surface Changes

Choose two of the four landforms shown here. Write a brief explanation for each on how you think they each might have been formed. Include at least two Earth systems in each of your explanations: **atmosphere**, **biosphere**, **hydrosphere**, and **geosphere**.

Waterfall

Beach

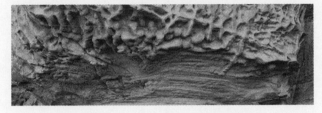

Sandstone Rock Formation

Sand Dune

Landform:

Landform:

2. How Islands Form

Explain how different Earth systems can interact to form islands.

- Include at least two of these terms: **biosphere**, **hydrosphere**, and **geosphere**.
- Include direct quotes from the Student Text.

3. Weathering, Erosion, and Deposition

Choose a landform to research. You can use your Student Text or find information on the Internet.

1) Draw a picture of this landform.

2) Write a short report on how this landform was formed.

- Include these terms: **weathering**, **erosion**, and **deposition**.
- Include any relevant Earth systems, such as the **atmosphere**, **biosphere**, **hydrosphere** or **geosphere**.

4. How Soil Forms

Explain how plants can grow in small cracks of rock that do not appear to contain soil.

- Include these terms: **weathering**, **erosion**, and **deposition**.
- Include any relevant Earth systems, such as **atmosphere**, **biosphere**, **geosphere**, and **hydrosphere**.

Turn an image of a landform into a diagram!

- Find an image of a landform, and paste it below.
- Add arrows and labels to show how Earth's systems interact to produce the landform.
- Underneath the diagram, describe which systems help produce the landform and how they interact to form it. Use the terms **weathering**, **erosion**, or **deposition** if they are involved with producing the landform.

How Do Farming and Industry Affect Earth's Systems?

Phenomenon: The miner is digging in the earth.

What questions do you have about this phenomenon?

After the lesson, use what you learned to explain this phenomenon.

1. Humans Affect Earth's Systems

1) Humans use fossil fuels every day for many different purposes. List two different ways you use fossil fuels.

2) Scientists and engineers are working to develop energy sources other than fossil fuels. What are some other energy sources scientists and engineers are researching?

2. Farming Affects Earth's Systems

Research how farming affects Earth's systems. Then, using the Student Text and your research, answer this question in a well-written paragraph: *How does farming affect Earth's systems?*

- Include these terms: **atmosphere**, **biosphere**, **hydrosphere**, and **geosphere**.
- Include quotes and cite your sources.

Print sources:

Digital sources:

3. Industry Affects Earth's Systems

Research one of these these industries:
nuclear power plant, **coal power plant**,
toy factory, or **electronics factory**.

Use at least one print and one digital source.
Write a paragraph on the affect it has on
Earth's systems.

- Include the terms: **atmosphere**,
  biosphere, **hydrosphere**, and **geosphere**.
- Include quotes and cite your sources.

Print sources:

Digital sources:

4. Scientists Study Pollution

Imagine you are a scientist studying pollution in a river.

1) Come up with three scientific questions you want to investigate. Remember that scientific questions are questions that are answered by data, not opinions.

2) What are three sources of data you can use to answer your scientific questions?

In this Small Group Investigation, you will observe some effects farming and industry have on Earth's systems. You will also model the effects the mining industry has on the geosphere by "mining" chocolate chips from chocolate chip cookies.

1) How many chips do you think you can mine in two minutes?

Using Mathematics and Computational Thinking

2) How many chips did you mine in two minutes?

Planning and Carrying Out Investigations

Number of chips: _____   Tool(s): _____

Total money earned: $_____ (number of chips x $1,000)

3) What tools and chip extraction strategies will you use in Round 2 to prevent damage to the environment while still extracting as many chips as possible?

Constructing Explanations and Designing Solutions

4) Record the number of chips you extracted in Round 2.

Planning and Carrying
Out Investigations

Number of chips: _____   Money earned: $_____ (number of chips x $1,000)

Number of broken pieces: _____   Money fined: $_____ (broken pieces x $200)

Total money earned: $_____ (money earned - money fined)

5) Compare your results from each round and answer the
following questions.

Analyzing and
Interpreting Data

a) Was the cookie environment damaged more in Round 1 or Round 2?

b) How did the $200 finc affect how you mined during Round 2?

c) How would you change your mining technique to make more money next time?

Use your notebook and Student Text to complete the
speech bubbles below.

Farmer

I help produce food for people every day. But farming
can impact Earth's systems. For example . . .

To collect information about the farmer's impact on Earth, I ask
scientific questions. One question I would ask is . . .

To find the answer to this question, I will . . .

Scientist

Miner

I mine resources from Earth's crust to make things like
sidewalks, spoons, and computers. But mining can impact
Earth's systems. For example . . .

To collect information about the miner's impact on Earth, I ask
scientific questions. One question I would ask is . . .

To find the answer to this question, I will . . .

Scientist

How Do People's Everyday Lives Affect Earth's Systems?

Phenomenon: You can't find books in nature, but they come from Earth's systems.

What questions do you have about this phenomenon?

After the lesson, use what you learned to explain this phenomenon.

1. Affecting Earth's Systems in the Morning

1) Describe what you did this morning when you woke up and got ready for school.

2) Which Earth systems did you interact with and how?

2. Affecting Earth's Systems at School

Come up with two ways you affect Earth's systems at school. Be clear and specific about which Earth system you are affecting, and how. Include these terms: **atmosphere**, **biosphere**, **hydrosphere**, and **geosphere**.

3. Affecting Earth's Systems at Home

1) List five objects that you use at home that are manufactured in factories.

2) What are some ways manufacturing objects in factories impact Earth systems?

In this Response Group, you will view examples of everyday activities and discuss how the activity affects Earth's systems with your group. Then you will brainstorm ways to reduce the negative impact the activity has on Earth.

1) Which Earth systems does eating breakfast affect? How are they affected?

Engaging in Argument from Evidence

2) Which Earth systems does driving to school affect? How are they affected?

Engaging in Argument from Evidence

3) Which Earth systems does playing during recess affect? How are they affected?

Engaging in Argument from Evidence

4) Which Earth systems does doing homework affect? How are they affected?

Engaging in Argument from Evidence

5) Which Earth systems does using electronics affect? How are they affected?

Engaging in Argument from Evidence

Interview a family member or teacher about an everyday activity.

- Choose an everyday activity. Record it below.
- Come up with three questions. Two questions should be about how the activity impacts Earth's systems. One question should be about how people can reduce the activity's impact. Record the questions below.
- Ask a family member or teacher the questions you came up with. Record who you talked to and their answers below.

Everyday activity: _____

Who I interviewed: _____

Question 1:

Answer 1:

Question 2:

Answer 2:

Question 3:

Answer 3:

What Can People Do to Protect Earth's Systems?

Phenomenon: Because of pollution, you can't drink this water.

What questions do you have about this phenomenon?

After the lesson, use what you learned to explain this phenomenon.

In this Small Group Investigation, you will act like an engineer to design and build a water filter using a set of materials. You will research different ways people protect Earth's systems with your group. You will create a podcast to report your research.

1) Define the problem your group is trying to solve. What are your criteria for a successful water filter, and what are your constraints?

Asking Questions and Defining Problems

Criteria:

Constraints:

2) Draw a diagram of your group's design. Label the materials, and explain how each material will help filter water.

Constructing Explanations
and Designing Solutions

3) Observe the effects of your filter on dirty water.

Analyzing and Interpreting Data

- Describe the water before it was filtered.
- Describe the water after it was filtered.
- Identify the criteria that were met and those that were not.

4) Draw a diagram of a new design for your water filter, and label
the materials. Describe the changes you made to the filter.

Constructing Explanations
and Designing Solutions

5) Observe the effects of your newly designed filter on dirty water.

Analyzing and
Interpreting Data

- Describe the water before it was filtered.
- Describe the water after it was filtered.
- Identify the criteria that were met and those that were not.

6) Conduct research to answer questions about the problem. Make sure to record the source you use to answer each question.

Obtaining, Evaluating, and Communicating Info

I am researching problems caused by _____

a) What are two ways the problem affects Earth's systems?

Source:

b) What is one solution people developed to protect Earth from the effects of this activity?

Source:

c) What are two ways the problem affects Earth's systems?

Source:

d) What is one solution people developed to protect Earth from the effects of this activity?

Source:

7) Write a script for your podcast. Your podcast will need to be one to two minutes long. Your script should include:

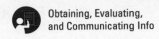
Obtaining, Evaluating, and Communicating Info

- an introduction to the problem.
- an explanation of how this problem affects Earth.
- a proposal for a solution that uses science ideas to protect Earth from this problem.
- an explanation of how this solution protects Earth.
- a conclusion.

1. Protecting Earth's Systems Is Important

Complete the flowchart. Explain how burning fossil fuels can result in polar bears being unable to meet their needs and becoming extinct. Be specific!

 Burning fossil fuels . . .

 . . . leads to more global warming and higher temperatures.

 Warmer temperatures on Earth lead to . . .

 . . . means that polar bears are unable to hunt for food.

 Polar bears are unable to meet their needs and become extinct.

2. Individuals Can Protect Earth's Systems

Think of some ways you can protect the environment.
Write a pledge to the environment. Be specific! Include
these terms: **conserve**, **protect**, **reduce**, **reuse**, and **recycle**.

I will . . .

I will . . .

I will . . .

3. Engineers Can Protect Earth's Systems

Scientists and engineers have come up with different methods to protect Earth's systems. Research one method. Then write a paragraph about what you learned. Use at least one print and one digital source. Include quotes and provide your sources.

Sources:

4. Communities Can Protect Earth's Systems

Interview a family member or librarian to find out what your community does to protect the environment. Then write a letter to your neighbor that encourages her or him to take advantage of some of these community programs. Be specific about which Earth system is being protected. Include these terms: **conserve** and **environment**.

5. Countries Can Protect Earth's Systems

Research what countries are doing to protect Earth systems. You may want to start your research with the U.S. Environmental Protection Agency or the United Nations Environment Programme. Write a report on a law or regulation that helps protect Earth systems. Include quotes and provide your sources.

Sources:

Jasmine lives in an area where cars and factories produce a lot of air pollution. She wanted to find information on how she can solve this problem.

Write a letter to Jasmine. Your letter should include:

- a salutation, such as *Dear Jasmine,*
- one example of how a community or person has tried to solve the problem. Make sure to include the source of this example.
- an explanation of where Jasmine can find more information on how other communities or individuals have tried to solve the problem.
- a closing line, such as *Your friend,*

What Is Matter Made Of?

Phenomenon: The balloon changes size and shape when the girl blows into it.

What questions do you have about this phenomenon?

After the lesson, use what you learned to explain this phenomenon.

In this Whole Class Investigation, you will observe and explain a series of investigations. Then you will develop a model that describes matter as consisting of particles that are too small to be seen.

1) What do you think happened to the salt when it mixed with water? What questions do you have?

? Asking Questions and Defining Problems

2) Explain why the balloon stretched when the teacher blew into it.

Constructing Explanations and Designing Solutions

3) Explain why the balloon got smaller when your teacher let all the air out.

Constructing Explanations and Designing Solutions

4) Explain why the ruler tipped to one side when your teacher let the air out of one of the balloons.

Constructing Explanations and Designing Solutions

5) Use the wood and newspaper investigation as evidence in an argument that air has weight.

Engaging in Argument from Evidence

6) Draw and label a diagram that models what air is made of.

Developing and
Using Models

7) Use your model to explain why a balloon inflates when you blow into it.

Developing and
Using Models

8) Use your model to explain why the balance tipped when one balloon was deflated.

Developing and Using Models

9) Use your model to explain why the wood broke when it was covered with newspaper.

Developing and Using Models

10) Use your model to explain what happened to the salt when it was mixed with water.

Developing and Using Models

1. Matter Is Made of Particles

1) Suppose you have a piece of matter sitting in a container. Draw an image that shows the matter as having many particles. Then, write a sentence describing your drawing.

Use these terms in your sentence: **matter**, **particle**, and **moving**.

2. States of Matter

1) Draw models that show the particles of matter during each state: solid, liquid, and gas. In your models, draw the matter inside a closed jar.

Solid	Liquid	Gas

2) Describe the differences between your different models. Use these terms in your answer: **solid**, **liquid**, **gas**, **fixed volume**, and **fixed shape**.

3. Matter Seems to Appear and Disappear

Using the images as a guide, describe how to make sugar crystals. Use these terms in your description: **substance**, **solid**, **liquid**, **dissolve**, **boil**, and **solution**.

4. Some Matter You Cannot See

1) Below is an image of a person inflating a balloon. Use small circles and arrows to show the air particles as they fill the balloon.

2) Explain how the air you breathe out can inflate the balloon. Use these terms in your answer: **weight**, **space**, **particles**, and **air**.

5. Odors Come From Matter

1) Suppose your teacher opened a bottle of perfume at one side of the classroom. Draw an image of the perfume particles when the bottle is opened, when you can smell the perfume from the middle of the classroom, and when you can smell the perfume at the other side of the classroom.

When the bottle is opened

When you can smell the perfume from the middle of the room

When you can smell the perfume at the other side of the room

2) Explain how perfume particles travel across the room. Use these terms in your answer: **perfume**, **particle**, **travel**, **air**, and **bump**.

Oh no! This bike has a flat tire.

What will happen when someone uses a bicycle pump to add air to the tire?

You cannot see the air that is pumped into a tire. But what evidence is there that air takes up space?

If bicycle tires are full of air, how is it possible for you to "ride on air"? Use your particle model of matter to explain how you can be held up by the air.

Why Are Materials Different?

Phenomenon: This ice looks different after it melts.

What questions do you have about this phenomenon?

After the lesson, use what you learned to explain this phenomenon.

1. There Are Many Different Materials

Suppose your teacher gives you a jar full of white powder. Your teacher tells you the powder is sugar, salt, baking soda, or flour. Which powder is in the jar?

You know that materials differ from each other in many ways. Come up with a method to identify the powder.

2. Different Types of Materials

1) Draw two diagrams. In the first diagram, show the particles in a solution. In the second, show particles in a solid mixture. In the diagrams, give each substance its own color.

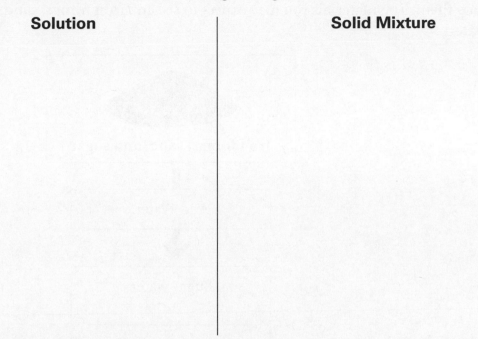

Solution	Solid Mixture

2) Write one solution and one solid mixture that you see in your daily life. Then use your diagrams to help explain why each is a solution and a solid mixture, and not a substance.

3. Separating Mixtures into Substances

Suppose you have a mixture of iron filings, sand, and sugar and you want to separate the three. Fill in the materials you expect to see at each step as you perform the actions shown to separate them. The materials you may expect to see are: **iron filings**, **sand**, **sugar**, and **sugar water**.

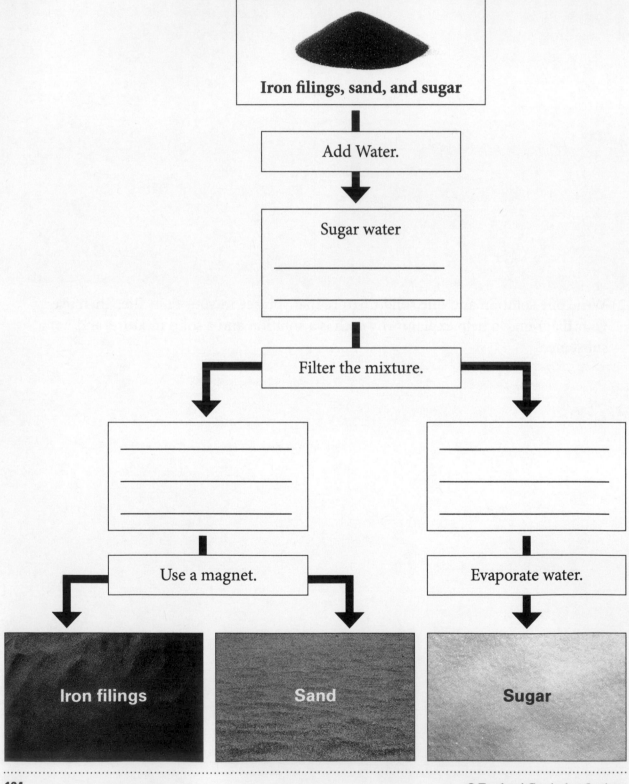

In this Experiential Exercise, you will continue to develop your model of matter. Your model will show that matter is made of particles too small to be seen. This is true of substances that are solid, liquid, and gas. Then you will model a mixture, which is a combination of two or more substances.

1) Draw and label a series of diagrams that show what happens when you drop a cube of sugar into a glass of water and stir the water. Then show what happens if you boil the sugar water.

Developing and Using Models

Sugar and water
particles before mixing

Sugar and water
particles after mixing

Sugar and water
particles after boiling
the sugar water

Your friend is confused. You told her that sugar water is a mixture of two substances. But she is looking at a glass of sugar water, and she only sees one substance!

Explain to your friend why there appears to only be one substance in the glass. Use these terms in your answer: **mixture**, **dissolve**, and **particles**.

What could you do to show your friend that the sugar particles still exist in the water?

© Teachers' Curriculum Institute

How Can Substances Be Identified?

Phenomenon: A sugar cube starts to disappear when dropped into a cup of water.

What questions do you have about this phenomenon?

After the lesson, use what you learned to explain this phenomenon.

1. Substances Have Identifiable Properties

1) You probably use properties to identify things without even realizing it! List two
   physical properties that you see when observing matter.

2) Sometimes you need more than your eyes to identify matter. Write two other properties
   that help you identify an object.

2. Properties You Can See

1) Gold and iron pyrite are two substances that are very similar but can be told apart by their properties. Draw a line to connect the property to the statement that best describes it.

Hardness

When scratched with a steel knife, gold will scratch and iron pyrite will not.

Color

Gold is bright yellow, and iron pyrite is pale yellow.

Reflectivity

When it is hit with a hammer, gold will flatten and iron pyrite will shatter.

Brittleness

Gold and iron pyrite are shiny.

2) Suppose you have a substance that is either gold or iron pyrite. You want to find out what you have. Choose two properties to test your substance with and explain why.

3. Some Properties Are Harder to See

Gold and iron pyrite are substances that look very similar but have very different properties. Pick a test from the list below that will help you tell gold and iron pyrite apart.

- burns easily
- bubbles in vinegar
- will rust when interacts with oxygen

Gold

Iron Pyrite

4. Scientists Use Properties to Identify Substances

Imagine you are a scientist trying to identify a substance that you just found. Think of five different tools for your science kit. Explain what property each tool will test for. Make sure you are testing more than one property.

Tool	Property

In this Small Group Investigation, you will observe unique properties of five different powders. Then you will use these properties to identify an unknown mystery powder.

1) Perform each of the four tests on each of your powders. Record your results on the table below.

Planning and Carrying Out Investigations

Powder	Appearance	Solubility	Vinegar	Iodine
Salt				
Talc				
Flour				
Baking Soda				
Baking Powder				

2) Test your unknown powder. Record your results.

Planning and Carrying Out Investigations

3) Which powder do you have? Use your results as evidence to support your argument.

Claim:

Evidence:

Reasoning:

You are designing an investigation to identify an unknown substance based on its properties. Below are four properties you want to test. Show how you would test it, and what sort of results you would expect to see. The first row is done as an example.

Property	How to Test	What Sort of Results Are You Looking For?
Hardness	Scratching it with a nail.	If the object is very hard, it will not be scratched by a nail.
Brittleness		
Solubility		
Reacts with Vinegar to Form a Gas		

How Do Scientists Know When Substances Change?

Phenomenon: When wood burns, its color changes.

What questions do you have about this phenomenon?

After the lesson, use what you learned to explain this phenomenon.

1. Changes in Matter Can Be Seen

Read the activities below. Circle the one that best matches this statement:
The property of matter changes because the substances in the materials have changed.

- changing matter from a liquid to a solid.
- mixing baking soda and vinegar to form a gas.
- scratching a piece of glass until it turns cloudy.

Explain your answer.

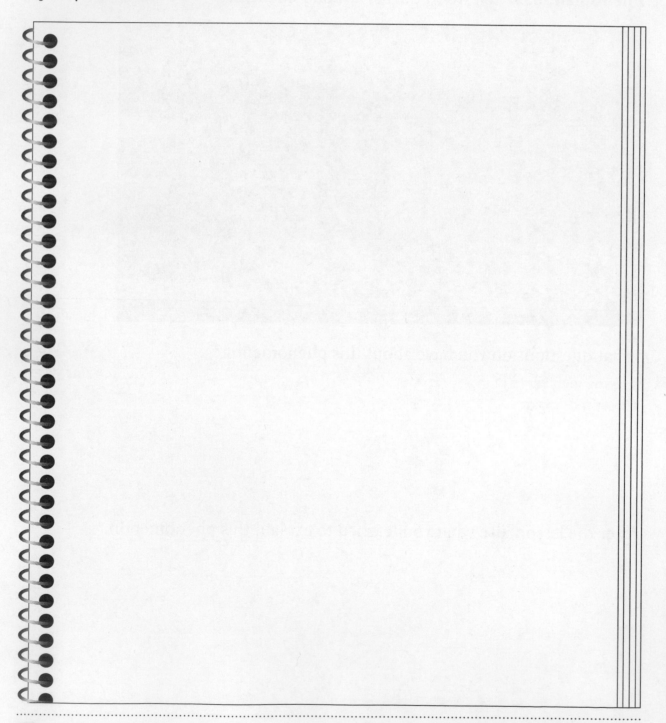

2. Substances Can Change State

1) Draw a diagram in each box showing the particles of water as a solid, liquid, or gas. Then, label the arrow with the correct state change: **melting**, **freezing**, **evaporation**, and **condensation**.

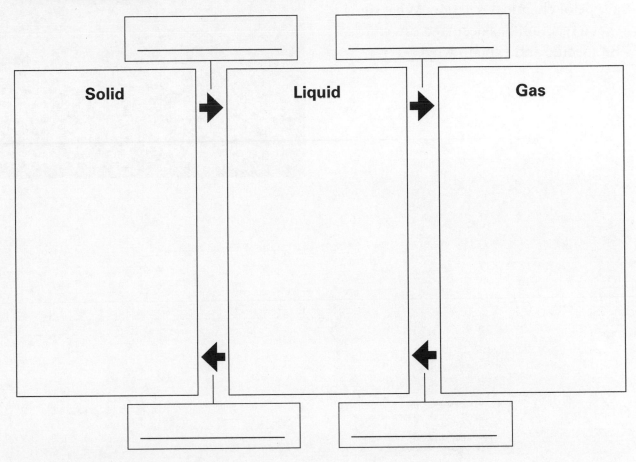

2) Using your diagrams, describe how the particles move as the matter changes from solid to liquid to gas.

3. New Substances Have New Properties

Here is an image of fireworks exploding in the night sky. Exploding fireworks are a type of chemical reaction. What signs that a reaction has occurred can you see? Be specific and explain why!

4. Substance Changes in Your Kitchen

Changes to substances happen all around you. Pick a change from the list below and write about it in more detail.

- water droplets forming on a glass of ice water.
- water puddles drying in the sun.
- muffins turning brown when you bake them.
- wood burning and forming ash.

In this Science Skill Builder, you will practice making observations and inferences. You will carefully observe a variety of situations in which substances are changing.

1) At each station, carefully observe the image you see, and fill out the matching row below.

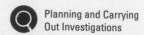
Planning and Carrying
Out Investigations

	What changes can you observe? (Describe how the properties are changing.)	Has a new substance been formed?	Why or why not? (Give evidence!)
		Yes No	
		Yes No	
		Yes No	
		Yes No	
		Yes No	
		Yes No	

© Teachers' Curriculum Institute

	What changes can you observe? (Describe how the properties are changing.)	Has a new substance been formed?	Why or why not? (Give evidence!)
		Yes No	
		Yes No	
		Yes No	
		Yes No	
		Yes No	
		Yes No	

You have observed many ways that substances can change.

Draw a picture of a substance changing state. Write a caption describing what is happening in your picture, and explain whether a new substance has been formed or not.

Draw a picture of a reaction that results in at least one new substance. Write a caption describing what is happening in your picture and describe what evidence you see that a new substance was formed.

© Teachers' Curriculum Institute

What Causes Substances to Change?

Phenomenon: Bubbles form when the baking soda in the flask comes into contact with vinegar.

What questions do you have about this phenomenon?

After the lesson, use what you learned to explain this phenomenon.

1. Changes to Substances Have Consistent Causes

1) When water is heated on a stove, it boils and begins to evaporate. What do you think will happen if juice is heated on a stove? Make a prediction!

> I predict . . .

2) Why did you make that prediction? Explain your thinking.

Hint: Do you have any previous experiences with heating liquids on a stove? Remember that changes have consistent causes!

2. Heating and Cooling Cause Changes

Suppose you are a substance drifting in the air as a gas. Write a story about being
- cooled to a liquid and then a solid, and
- heated back to a liquid and a gas

Include these terms in your story: **particles**, **melt**, **freeze**, **evaporate**, **condense**, **expand**, and **contract**. Be creative!

_____

_____

_____

_____

_____

_____

_____

_____

_____

_____

_____

_____

_____

_____

_____

_____

3. Mixing Substances Causes Changes

1) Draw a diagram in each box to show how mixing can **dissolve substances**. Use particles in your diagrams.

Before Mixing	**After Mixing**

2) Draw a diagram in each box to show how mixing can **cause reactions**. Use particles in your diagrams. Use a different color for each substance!

Before Mixing	**After Mixing**

4. Why You Use a Refrigerator

Change happens all around you. Write about a change of matter that you see in everyday life. Choose from the list below. Explain why you think the substance is changing. Describe how heating, cooling, or mixing can affect the substance.

- cooking food so it is edible.
- putting food in the refrigerator so it doesn't spoil.
- making juice from juice mix.

In this Science Skill Builder, you will practice making observations and inferences. You will carefully observe a variety of situations in which substances are changing.

1) What is a fair test? How can you make an investigation a fair test?

Planning and Carrying Out Investigations

2) Write down the question you are trying to investigate. Then, identify the data, or evidence, you will use to answer the investigation question.

Planning and Carrying Out Investigations

3) List as many different mixtures of the four substances as you can. You can include two, three, or all four substances in each mixture.

Using Mathematics and Computational Thinking

4) You will test eight mixtures in this activity. Record the substances. Test each of the mixtures and record your observations. Which properties, if any, changed? Do you think a new substance formed?

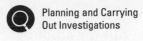

Planning and Carrying Out Investigations

	Substances	Observations	New Substance Formed?
1			Yes No
2			Yes No
3			Yes No
4			Yes No
5			Yes No
6			Yes No
7			Yes No
8			Yes No

5) Calculate the total amount of each substance you will need. List out the amount of each substance for each test. Then add up the amounts to determine the total amount you will need to get from the teacher.

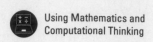

Using Mathematics and Computational Thinking

Test	Powder A	Powder B	Liquid A	Liquid B
Example	1 Spoonful	1 Spoonful	40 mL	0 mL
1				
2				
3				
4				
5				
6				
7				
8				
Total				

6) Which mixtures that the class tested did a new substance form in? Explain your conclusions using your observations as evidence.

Analyzing and Interpreting Data

7) Which substances reacted to form new substances? In any of the class's tests, could you have removed a substance and still caused a new substance to form? Support your argument with evidence.

Engaging in Argument from Evidence

For each of the images below, explain the changes in substances that are occurring and whether a new substance has been created or not. Then explain what caused the changes to occur.

Frozen waterfall

Tablet dissolving in water

Burnt toast

How Do Changes to Substances Affect Their Weights?

Phenomenon: When a reaction creates bubbles, the balloon inflates.

What questions do you have about this phenomenon?

After the lesson, use what you learned to explain this phenomenon.

In this Whole Class Investigation, you will measure the weight of substances before and after causing a change. By measuring and graphing quantities, you will discover what happens to the weight of substances during different kinds of changes.

1) First, record the weight of the cup with frozen water. Then, predict how the total weight will be affected by melting. Explain why you think the weight will or will not change. After the water has melted, record the weight in the correct column.

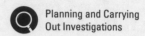 Planning and Carrying Out Investigations

	Cup with Frozen Water	After Melting
Weight (grams)		

I predict...

2) Record the weight of the cup with liquid water in the first column below. Then, explain how you think the total weight will be affected by freezing. After the water has frozen, record the weight of the cup below.

Planning and Carrying Out Investigations

	Cup with Liquid Water	After Freezing
Weight (grams)		

I think...

3) Measure and record the weight of the salt, water, cup, and the bowl before and after mixing the salt and water.

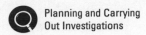
Planning and Carrying Out Investigations

	Before Mixing	**After Mixing**
Total Weight (grams)		

4) Create a bar graph that shows the total weight of the salt, water, cup, and bowl both before and after mixing. Give your graph a title. Color-code the weights and label them in a key.

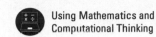
Using Mathematics and Computational Thinking

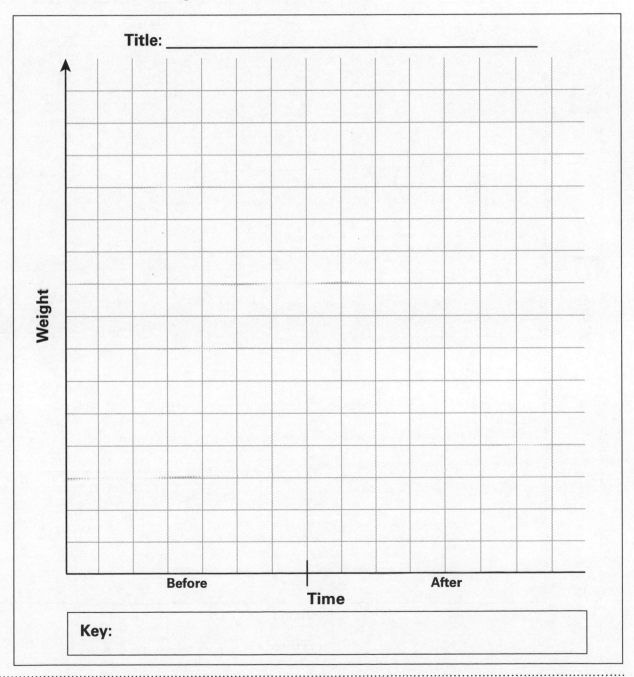

Title: _____

Weight

Before   After

Time

Key:

5) Measure and record the weight of the jar of cream before mixing, during mixing, and after it turns to butter.

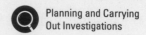 Planning and Carrying Out Investigations

	Before Mixing (cream)	During Mixing (whipped cream)	After Mixing (butter)
Weight (grams)			

6) Create a bar graph that shows the weight of the cream before, during, and after it was separated into butter.

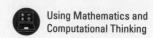 Using Mathematics and Computational Thinking

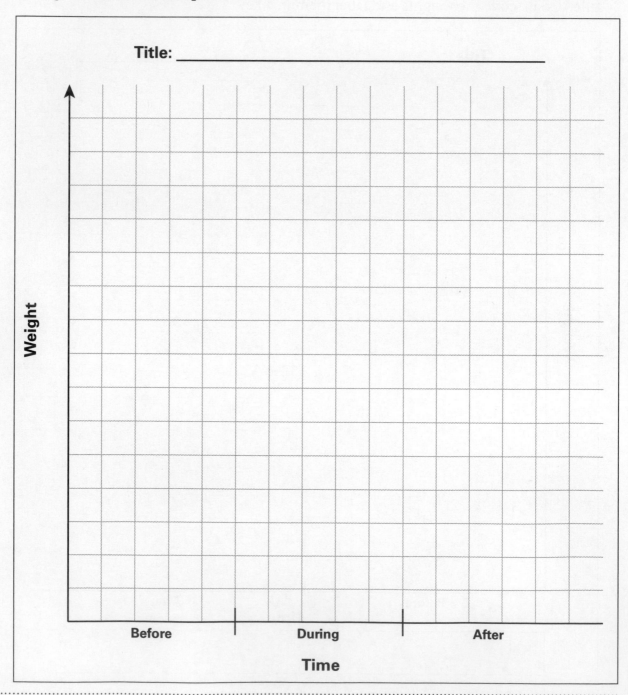

7) Using your model of the particle nature of matter, explain why the total weight did not change when you mixed salt and water, as well as when you separated cream into butter.

Developing and Using Models

8) When four antacid tablets were added to water, what happened to the total weight? Why?

Analyzing and Interpreting Data

9) How might you change the test with the antacid tablet to make its results match your other two tests?

Planning and Carrying Out Investigations

1. Matter Is Conserved

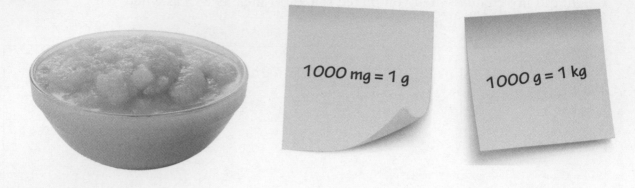

Suppose you wanted to make apple sauce. Your recipe gives the measurements in kilograms (kg) and milligrams (mg), but your scale uses grams (g)!

1) The recipe asks for 0.8 kg of apples. How many grams of apples should you measure?

2) The recipe asks for 900 mg of salt. How many grams of salt should you measure?

3) The recipe asks for 0.8 kg of apples, 0.6 kg of water, and 90 mg of salt. When you cook the ingredients together it turns into a thick sauce. How many grams of apple sauce do you have? Remember that matter is conserved.

2. Weight and Changes in Temperature

1) Carefully look at the arrows showing state changes. Draw a diagram in each box showing the particles of matter at each state. Remember that matter is conserved!

2) The diagram below shows the state changes. Label each box with the state of matter.

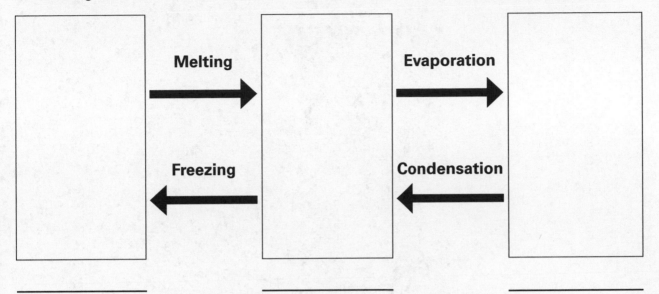

3) Describe a way to test the conservation of matter as the state changes. Explain any measurements you would make and why the test would work.

3. Weight and Changes from Mixing

Look at this image of vinegar reacting with baking soda to form carbon dioxide. Baking soda is poured into the balloon, and vinegar is poured into the plastic bottle. The baking soda is then tipped into the plastic bottle. Carbon dioxide forms and begins to fill the balloon.

How is matter conserved? Think about what happened to the balloon after the baking soda and vinegar started to react.

4. Science Assumes All Matter is Conserved

1) Describe what is happening to the matter in each image. What pattern can you observe? Use **weight** and **conserved** in your answer.

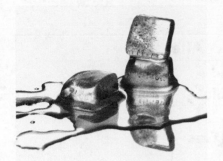  

2) Suppose you dissolved an antacid tablet in a glass of water and measured the weight. You would find that the weight changes! How does this observation fit with the pattern that matter is conserved?

Hint: Look at the image. Notice the bubbles being formed and where they are going.

You decide to perform the antacid investigation again, and this time you remember to capture and weigh the gas. But you forgot to record the weight of the water after the tablet has finished dissolving! Using the given weights, calculate how much the water and tablet weigh. Then, create a bar graph that shows how the weight changed.

Before (g)		After (g)	
Water	100	**Water and Antacid Tablet**	
Antacid Tablet	5	**Balloon and Gas**	12
Balloon	10		

Create a bar graph that shows the weights of the components before and after the reaction. Give your graph a title. Also color-code the components and label them in a key.

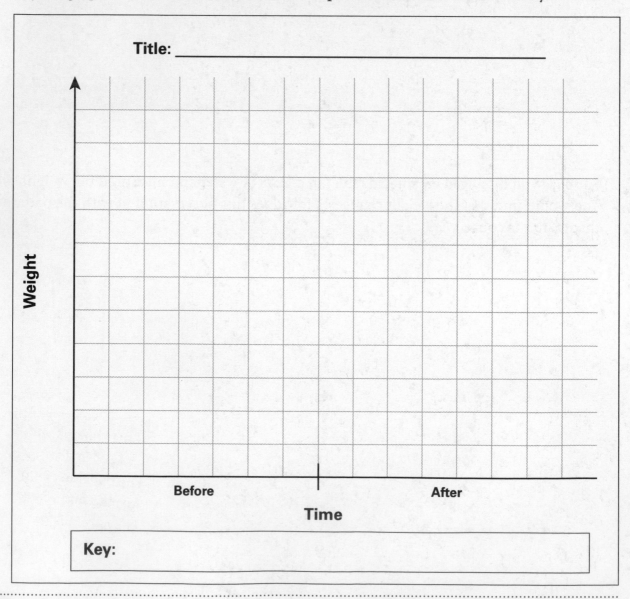

How Do Engineers Improve Materials?

Phenomenon: Concrete makes a stronger floor than dirt.

What questions do you have about this phenomenon?

After the lesson, use what you learned to explain this phenomenon.

1. Properties Have Different Uses

Suppose you need cloth for making a piece of clothing.

- List at least three criteria.
- List at least three constraints.

Criteria:

Constraints:

2. Engineers Choose the Best Material

Look at the images. Each shows a substance that you might use for clothing. Pick the material you think is best. Explain your reasoning. Refer back to the criteria and constraints you considered in Section 1.

Cotton

Straw

Leaves

Wool

3. Engineers Create New Materials

Engineers have designed materials for clothing that you might be wearing! Choose one of the materials listed below and research it. Then, write a paragraph about what you learned. Use at least one print and one digital source. Include quotes and provide your sources.

- Polyester
- Nylon
- Spandex
- Acrylic

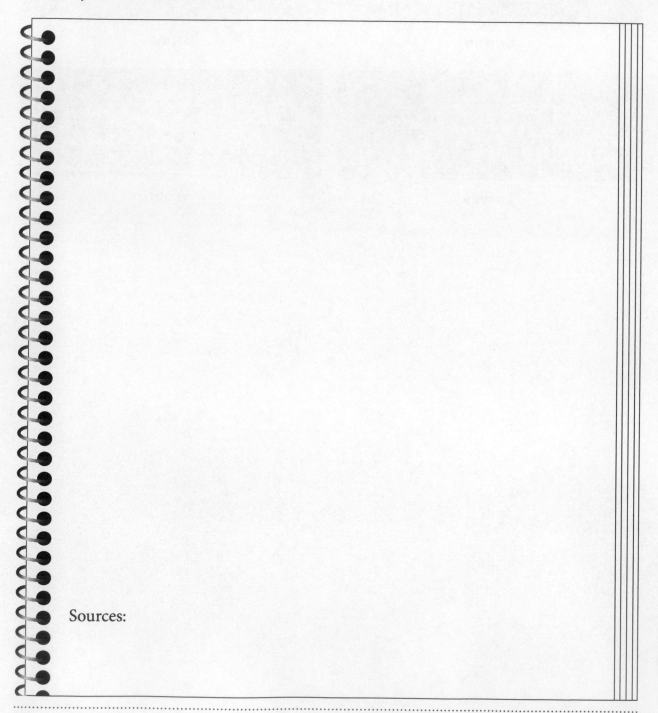

Sources:

© Teachers' Curriculum Institute

4. Engineer Your Own Material

1) You are getting ready to engineer your own cloth! Think about the materials you might use. Think about the constraints and criteria for your cloth. Come up with three tests for your new cloth.

2) Suppose you have engineered your own cloth. You've tested the cloth to see what properties it has. You find out that the cloth is warm, becomes scratchy after washed, and falls apart after being washed twice.

Based on these tests, what other criteria or constraints would you add?

In this Small Group Investigation, you will make glue from flour and water. You will use the engineering design process to identify what makes good glue and then test different processes to find the best one.

1) List the properties glue should have to be effective. These are your criteria for your glue.

Asking Questions and Defining Problems

2) What constraints, or limitations, do you have on designing your glue?

Asking Questions and Defining Problems

3) How can you test each of the properties you listed in your criteria? How will you make sure your tests are fair tests?

Planning and Carrying Out Investigations

4) What variables can you adjust in your glue recipe?

Asking Questions and Defining Problems

5) Record the recipes you used and how many washers each one held. You should only change one variable between each recipe.

Planning and Carrying Out Investigations

Recipe	Variables				Test
	Flour	Water	Stir Time	Dry Time	Number of Washers
Control Recipe					
1st Recipe					
2nd Recipe					
3rd Recipe					

6) How did you change your recipe? Why did you make that change?

Constructing Explanations and Designing Solutions

Your turn! Think of a problem that could be solved by developing a new object or tool. It could be a big problem that affects the world, or a small problem that affects your daily life.

Describe the problem.

Now define the problem by listing several criteria for success. (How will you know you have solved the problem?)

Now list several constraints. (How are you limited by time, cost, or materials?)

What steps would take you take after you have finished defining the problem above?

What Does Gravity Do?

Phenomenon: No matter where you jump on Earth, you will land on the ground.

What questions do you have about this phenomenon?

After the lesson, use what you learned to explain this phenomenon.

In this Experiential Exercise, you will investigate the effect of gravity. Then, using evidence from tests and images, you will support an argument that the gravitational force of the Earth is directed toward the Earth's center.

1) Write a claim that answers this question: *What does gravity do?*   Engaging in Argument from Evidence

2) Give two pieces of evidence that support your claim. (Hint: Think about the activities we did in class and your own personal experiences.)   Engaging in Argument from Evidence

3) Modify your claim. What observations did you use to revise your claim?   Engaging in Argument from Evidence

1. Gravity Pulls You Toward Earth's Center

1) Draw and label a diagram of Earth from space that illustrates this passage from the Student Text:

> Wherever you stand on Earth, gravity is pulling you straight down toward its center. So, "down" is always in the direction gravity pulls. "Up" is always the direction opposite to the pull of gravity.

2) List two pieces of evidence described in the Student Text that support this argument:

> Gravity pulls down toward the center of Earth.

2. Gravity Causes Meteors

Draw and label a diagram showing how Earth's gravity creates meteors ("shooting stars") and meteorites.

Make sure the following items are in your drawing: **atmosphere**, **gravity**, **meteor**, **meteorites**, and **space**.

3. Gravity Is Strongest at Earth's Surface

You know that Earth has a gravitational field that reaches beyond Earth's surface.

Answer this question in a well-written paragraph: *Is gravity as strong far away as it is close to Earth?*

To support your argument, quote evidence from the Student Text.

_____

_____

_____

_____

_____

_____

_____

_____

_____

_____

_____

_____

_____

_____

_____

4. All Objects Have Gravity

1) Draw and label a model that shows Earth orbiting the sun and the moon orbiting Earth.

2) In one complete sentence, explain why Earth orbits the sun.

5. Weight Is the Force of Gravity

1) Read these four statements. Then circle the one that is true.

    A) I weigh the same on Earth and the moon.

    B) I weigh more on Earth than on the moon.

    C) I weigh more on the moon than on Earth.

    D) I weigh nothing, except on Earth.

2) Explain why the statement you chose is true. Make sure to discuss gravity!

Fill out the table. Use complete sentences.

Engaging in Argument from Evidence

Object	How Does Gravity Affect This Object?	What Evidence Supports Your Claim?
A ball tossed in the air		
A meteorite in the atmosphere		
The moon in space		

Why Is the Sun Brighter Than Other Stars?

Phenomenon: You can see the stars at night but not during the day.

What questions do you have about this phenomenon?

After the lesson, use what you learned to explain this phenomenon.

In this Small Group Investigation, you will see how the distance affects how bright a flashlight appears on paper. Then you will model observing the stars from Earth. Using this model as evidence, you will construct an argument about how the brightness of stars varies depending on their distance from Earth.

1) Use the graph paper to observe how the size of the circle of light relates to the distance from graph paper. Then complete the chart. Be detailed in your observations!

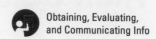

Obtaining, Evaluating, and Communicating Info

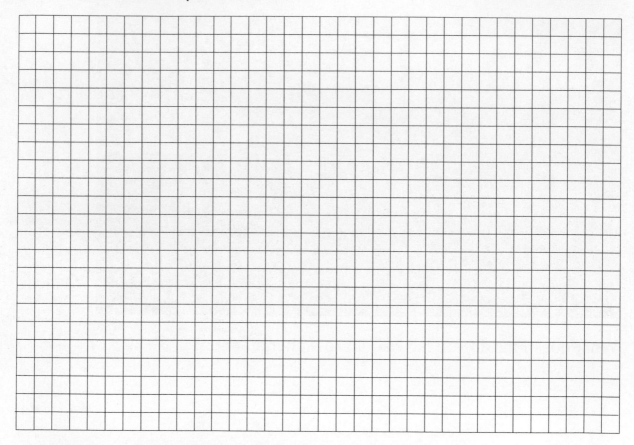

Distance to Graph Paper	Size of Circle	Other Observations (Hint: Look at the brightness of the circle!)
10 cm		
60 cm		

2) What conclusions can you make about how distance, size, and brightness of light are related? Be sure to include evidence.

Engaging in Argument from Evidence

```

```

3) Using this image, model how light from the sun and other stars shine on Earth. Label each resulting circle of light with the distance you chose to shine it from, and compare the brightness.

Developing and Using Models

4) What conclusions can you make about how light from stars shine on Earth? How are they the same or different from the conclusions you reached with a flashlight?

Engaging in Argument from Evidence

```

```

5) Record your observations for each of the following scenarios.

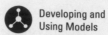

Developing and
Using Models

Scenario	Description	Observations
1	1 flashlight near Earth	
2	2 flashlights shining from the same side 1 near Earth 1 far from Earth	
3	1 flashlight far from Earth	
4	3 flashlights, 1 shining from opposite side as others	

6) Come up with a theory on why you can see the stars from Earth. Write one way you can test this theory.

Planning and Carrying Out Investigations

7) Which model was most accurate to describe how the sun and stars shine light on Earth? Explain why.

Developing and Using Models

1. Light from Stars Travels to Earth

1) Why do stars farther from Earth appear dimmer than stars closer to Earth?

In your answer, use these terms: **light rays**, **brighter**, **dimmer**, and **distance**.

2) Explain why the sun appears to be so much brighter than other stars we can see on Earth.

2. Measuring Distances in Space

1) What are light-years, and why do scientists use them?

2) Why does it make sense to estimate that the sun is 0 light-years from Earth? Does this mean that the sun is close to Earth?

3) A star called Betelgeuse is 643 light-years away from Earth. This is 6.08×10^{15} kilometers (km) from Earth. Write this number in standard form.

3. Distance Affects a Star's Apparent Brightness

1) What is apparent brightness? Why is it hard to tell how bright a star really is?

2) The two stars in the diagram below are the exact same size. But they will look different from Earth!

   a) Label the star that will appear brighter by writing "Brighter" near it.

   b) Label the star that will appear dimmer by writing "Dimmer" near it.

   c) Support your answer by drawing rays of light from each star to Earth.

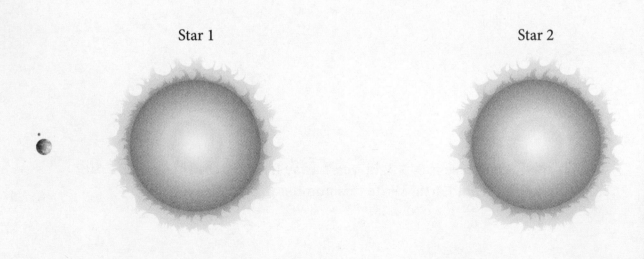

Star 1   Star 2

4. Other Factors Affect a Star's Apparent Brightness

Suppose your parent or guardian took you on a camping trip far from the city's lights. One night you looked into the night sky, and you both noticed some bright stars and some dim stars.

Now is your chance to shine! How would *you* explain the apparent brightness of the stars? Make sure to discuss all three factors you learned about.

One of your friends claims, "The sun is obviously the biggest and brightest star in the universe!"

Draw and label a diagram that shows why the sun appears so much bigger and brighter than all other stars. Make sure to draw and label each of the following:

- Earth
- the sun
- a star (other than the sun)
- light rays

Use your diagram as evidence to refute your friend's claim.

Why Is There Day and Night?

Phenomenon: Daytime is bright, and nighttime is dark.

What questions do you have about this phenomenon?

After the lesson, use what you learned to explain this phenomenon.

In this Whole Class Investigation, you will use a model of the sun and Earth to construct an explanation for why there is day and night, how it can be a different time of day on different parts of Earth, and why the sun seems to move across the sky each day.

1) Draw and label a diagram that shows how Earth's rotation causes day and night.

Developing and Using Models

2) Explain why the sun appears to move across the sky.

Constructing Explanations and Designing Solutions

The sun appears to move across the sky because . . .

3) Draw and label a diagram that shows how it can be a different time of day in different places.

Developing and
Using Models

1. Earth Spins on Its Axis

Write a poem about how Earth's rotation causes day and night. Be sure to use these terms: **rotate**, **axis**, **sun**, **move**, and **Earth**.

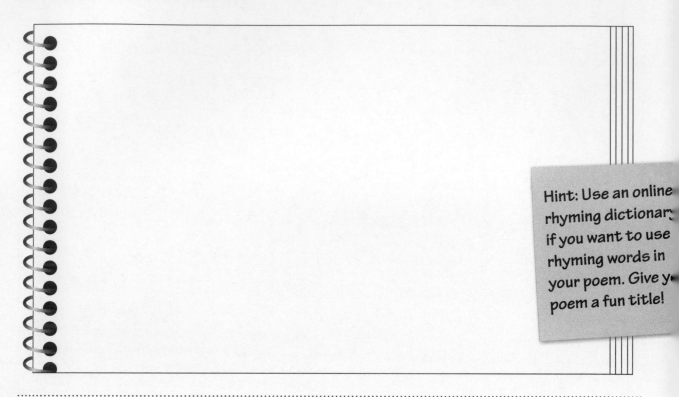

Hint: Use an online rhyming dictionary if you want to use rhyming words in your poem. Give your poem a fun title!

2. Earth's Rotation Causes Day and Night

Draw and label a model that shows how Earth's rotation causes night and day.

Be sure to include these labels on your model: **day**, **Earth**, **night**, **rotate**, **sun**, and **sunlight**.

3. It Is a Different Time of Day in Different Places

Complete each of these tasks:

- Write "Noon" (12 PM) and "Eastern" in the eastern time zone of the United States.
- Label the remaining five time zones.
- Finally, write the correct times in each time zone, assuming it is noon Eastern Time.

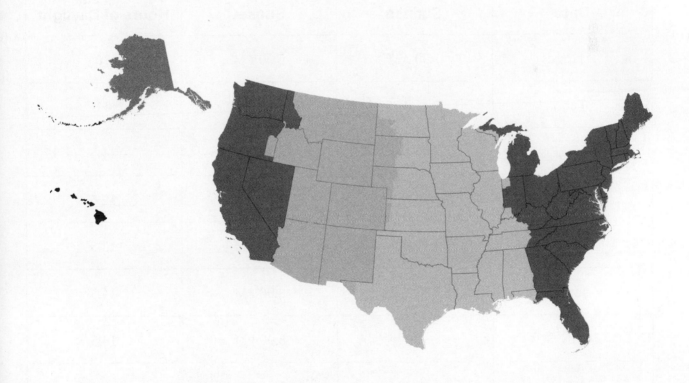

4. The Amount of Daylight Changes During the Year

Read this description of an investigation conducted by a student. Then be prepared to analyze her data!

> Kim wanted to investigate how daylight changes throughout the year. She followed these procedures:
> - She chose a location close to home that she would observe once a month.
> - On the first day of each month, she observed and recorded the sunrise time.
> - The same day, she observed and recorded the sunset time.
> - Then she figured out the number of hours of daylight.

Date	Sunrise	Sunset	Hours of Daylight
Jan.	7:30 AM	5:30 PM	10
Feb.	7:15 AM	6:15 PM	11
Mar.	7:00 AM	6:30 PM	11.5
Apr.	6:30 AM	7:00 PM	12.5
May	5:45 AM	7:15 PM	13.5
June	5:30 AM	8:00 PM	14.5
July	5:30 AM	8:00 PM	14.5
Aug.	5:45 AM	7:45 PM	14
Sep.	6:00 AM	7:00 PM	13
Oct.	6:30 AM	6:30 PM	12
Nov.	7:00 AM	6:00 PM	11
Dec.	7:15 AM	5:15 PM	10

1) Carefully observe the table on the previous page. Then create a bar graph of the data from Kim's investigation.

- Title the graph "Hours of Daylight in Phoenix, Arizona."
- Label the x-axis "Month."
- Label the y-axis "Daylight (hours)."
- Graph the amount of daylight for each month.

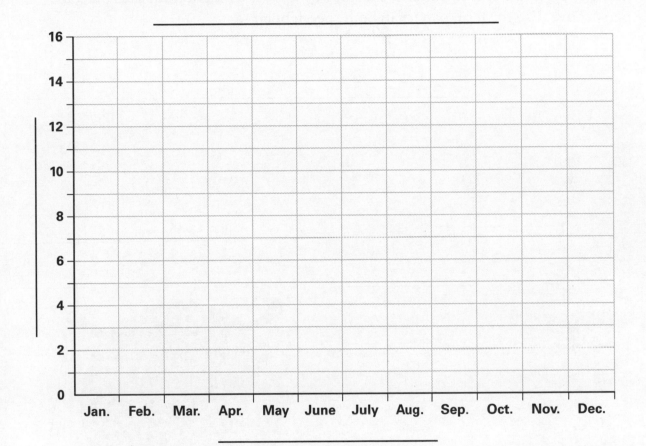

2) Explain how daylight changes during a year. Make sure to describe the pattern of daylight during all four seasons. Give specific evidence from the data gathered during Kim's investigation.

Look at the two people "standing" on Earth in the model below.

On the diagram,

- Draw and label rays of sunlight from the sun to Earth.
- Write "Day" next to the person who would be experiencing daylight.
- Write "Night" next to the person who would be experiencing darkness.

In the appropriate speech bubbles, explain why it is day or night from each person's perspective. Use the term pattern in both speech bubbles.

How Do Shadows Change During the Day and Year?

Phenomenon: Shadows move and change length throughout the day.

What questions do you have about this phenomenon?

After the lesson, use what you learned to explain this phenomenon.

In this Small Group Investigation, you will observe a model to see how Earth's rotation causes shadows to change length and direction. Then you will build a sundial, which is a tool that uses shadows to tell time!

1) Measure the length of the shadow the paperclip casts on the globe at five different simulated times: sunrise, midmorning, noon, midafternoon, and sunset. Repeat for three different locations.

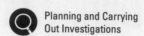

Planning and Carrying Out Investigations

		Shadow at Sunrise		Shadow at Midmorning		Shadow at Noon		Shadow at Midafternoon		Shadow at Sunset	
		Direction	Length (cm)	Direction	Length (cm)	Direction	Length (cm)	Direction	Length (cm)	Direction	Length (cm)	
Location 1												
Location 2												
Location 3												

2) Create a bar graph that shows the length of the shadows at the three different locations during our simulation. Use a different color for each location and show that color in the key. Make sure your graph has a **title** and that the **axes** are labeled.

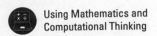
Using Mathematics and
Computational Thinking

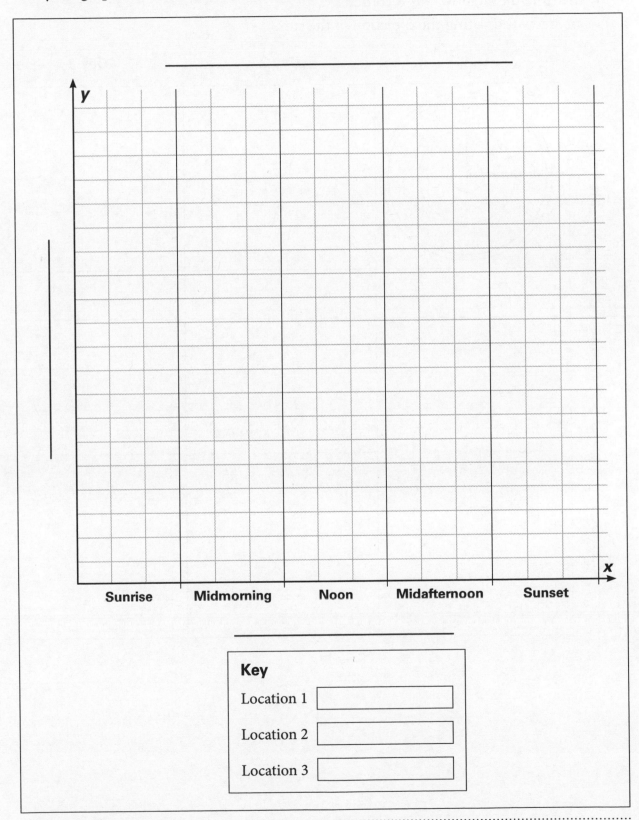

Key

Location 1

Location 2

Location 3

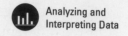
Analyzing and
Interpreting Data

3) In each box below, draw a diagram of your sundial at that day and
time. For each diagram, include
- the shadow on the sundial.
- the time the shadow was recorded.
- an arrow indicating the direction of the sun.

	Day 1	**Day 2**	**Day 3**
Morning			
Noon			
Afternoon			

4) Using your diagram as evidence, construct an argument for why sundials are an effective method for telling time. Use the motion of the sun in your explanation.

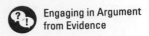

Engaging in Argument from Evidence

1. Shadows Follow a Daily Pattern

Create a bar graph of this data from an investigation:

- Title the graph "Shadow Lengths by Time of Day." Label the x-axis "Time."
- Label the y-axis "Shadow Length (cm)."
- Graph the observed length of the shadow at the ten different times of day.

	Time									
Shadow Length (cm)	8 AM	9 AM	10 AM	11 AM	12 PM	1 PM	2 PM	3 PM	4 PM	5 PM
	110	73	52	29	8	31	59	78	112	185

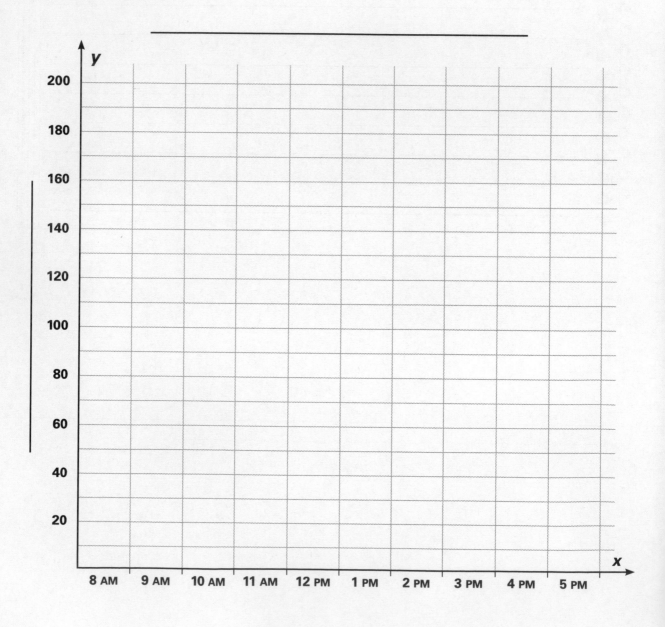

2. Shadows Follow a Yearly Pattern

Label the parts of this diagram. Make sure to use these terms: **Shortest day of winter, Day and night equal, Longest day of summer, Shadow on longest day of summer,** and **Shadow on shortest day of winter.**

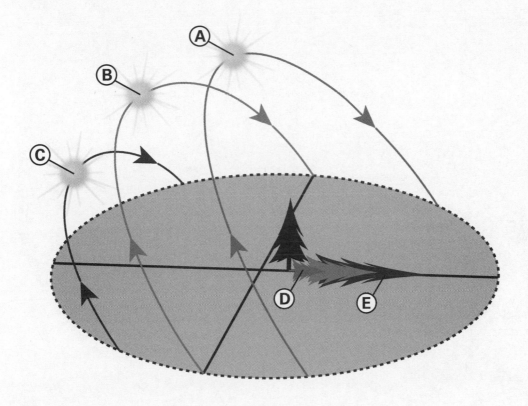

A) _____

B) _____

C) _____

D) _____

E) _____

3. Using Shadows to Measure Time

Explain the parts of a sundial and how it works.

Include these terms in your explanation: **sundial**, **time**, **shadow**, **wedge**, **base**, and **time intervals**.

4. Shadows Point in Different Directions in Different Places

Complete the speech bubbles for each person.

I live in the Northern Hemisphere.
My shadow always points

_____

because...

I live in the Southern Hemisphere.
My shadow always points

_____

because...

Northern Hemisphere

Southern Hemisphere

Look at this photograph. It was taken in the morning as these students walked to school.

Using what you have learned about shadow patterns, explain the following:

*   In what direction are their shadows pointing? Are they long or short in the morning?

*   In what direction are the students walking? How do you know?

*   Suppose the students stop walking and stand here for the rest of the day. What will happen to their shadows?

*   Why do shadows change throughout the day?

How Do Stars Seem to Move During the Night and Year?

Phenomenon: You see Orion in one part of the sky. Later that night, it is on the other side of the sky.

What questions do you have about this phenomenon?

After the lesson, use what you learned to explain this phenomenon.

1. Star Patterns Form Pictures in the Sky

Find a picture of a constellation in a reference book or on the Internet. Some constellations you might choose from include: Scorpius, Orion, or Cassiopeia.

1) In the space below:
- write the name of the constellation you researched.
- draw the pattern of stars in this constellation.

2) In the space below:
- explain why the pattern of stars you choose is called by its constellation name.
- list the sources (books or Internet sites) that helped you find this information.

2. Stars Seem to Move During the Night

Write a paragraph that explains how the stars appear to move throughout the night. Make sure to explain whether the stars are actually moving or not!

Use the following terms in your answer: **appear**, **counter-clockwise**, **Earth**, **north**, **rotate**, **semicircle**, and **stars**.

3. Using Stars and Star Patterns to Navigate

Look carefully at this image. Then answer each question in a complete sentence.

1) If you look at the sky at many different times at night, will it look like the constellations, such as the Big Dipper and Little Dipper, are moving? How?

2) Where is Polaris in this image? Does it move during the night?

3) The Student Text says, "Like people have been doing for thousands of years, you can use the stars to find your way around." Explain how people could use the stars to navigate. Give evidence from this image.

4. Constellations Seem to Change With the Seasons

Looking at Orion

Looking at Scorpius

Puzzle: A man stands on a road in Iowa looking up at the night sky. On one night he sees the constellation Orion. But on another night, at the same time and on the same road, he sees the constellation Scorpius.

Explain how this is possible. Use these terms in your explanation: **Earth**, **Northern Hemisphere**, **Orion**, **pattern**, and **Scorpius**.

5. People Use Constellations to Tell Stories

Write your own story or myth about the constellation Ursa Major.

In your myth, include a situation, characters, a sequence of events, and a conclusion.

6. Scientists Use Star Charts to Map the Sky

Complete the speech bubble for the astronomer in this image.

Use the following terms in your answer: **constellation**, **locate**, and **pattern**.

Star patterns are useful to me because...

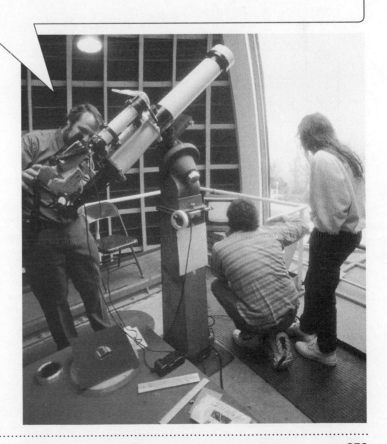

In this Experiential Exercise, you will model how the stars appear to change position over the course of a night and a year. You will also graph and analyze data about how high in the sky certain stars are throughout the year.

1) Use the data in the table to create a line graph showing how high above the horizon these four constellations are at different times of year in the Northern Hemisphere.

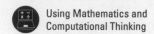
Using Mathematics and Computational Thinking

- Give the graph a title.
- Label the x-axis "Month."
- Label the y-axis "Altitude (degrees)."
- Add a key.
- Using a different color for each constellation, graph and connect the points.

	Jan.	Feb.	Mar.	Apr.	May	June	July	Aug.	Sep.	Oct.	Nov.	Dec.
Leo	11 °	35 °	53 °	62 °	50 °	28 °	6 °	0 °	0 °	0 °	0 °	0 °
Scorpius	0 °	0 °	0 °	0 °	12 °	22 °	21 °	10 °	0 °	0 °	0 °	0 °
Pisces	5 °	0 °	0 °	0 °	0 °	0 °	0 °	21 °	42 °	53 °	46 °	28 °
Orion	44 °	36 °	19 °	0 °	0 °	0 °	0 °	0 °	0 °	0 °	19 °	36 °

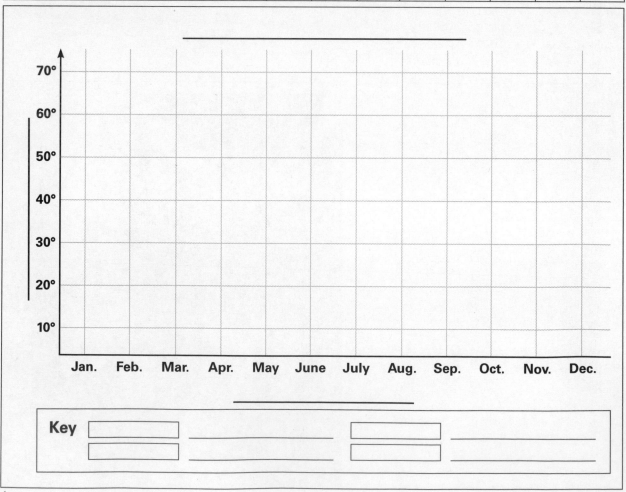

2) Explain why we see different stars throughout the year.
Support your explanation with evidence from the model you
experienced in class and the data you graphed.

Constructing Explanations
and Designing Solutions

Suppose it's a warm summer night. There are no clouds and you have a clear view of the stars in the night sky. One of your friends looks up and complains, "Where is the constellation Orion? I haven't seen it at all tonight!"

Create a diagram that models why you cannot see the stars in Orion (such as Betelgeuse) during the summer.

Your model should include:

- the sun.
- Earth in its orbit.
- labels showing which side of Earth is day, and which side is night.
- a label showing the direction you would have to look to see the stars in Orion.

How Does the Moon Seem to Move and Change Shape?

Phenomenon: The moon looks different on different days.

What questions do you have about this phenomenon?

After the lesson, use what you learned to explain this phenomenon.

1. The Sun Lights Up the Moon

1) Draw and label a diagram that shows the following:

- Earth orbiting around the sun.
- The moon orbiting around Earth.
- The sun lighting up part of Earth (creating day and night).
- The sun lighting up part of the moon.

2) Explain your diagram.

2. The Moon Rises and Sets in a Pattern

Day	Moonrise	Moonset	Day	Moonrise	Moonset
1	5:24 AM	4:28 PM	16	5:12 PM	6:23 AM
2	6:29 AM	5:24 PM	17	6:01 PM	7:12 AM
3	7:33 AM	6:25 PM	18	6:52 PM	7:57 AM
4	8:34 AM	7:30 PM	19	7:44 PM	8:39 AM
5	9:29 AM	8:37 PM	20	8:36 PM	9:18 AM
6	10:20 AM	9:43 PM	21	9:28 PM	9:55 AM
7	11:05 AM	10:48 PM	22	10:20 PM	10:29 AM
8	11:46 AM	11:50 PM	23	11:13 PM	11:03 AM
9	12:24 PM	12:15 AM	24	11:50 PM	11:45 AM
10	1:02 PM	12:50 AM	25	12:07 AM	12:11 PM
11	1:39 PM	1:48 AM	26	1:03 AM	12:48 PM
12	2:17 PM	2:46 AM	27	2:02 AM	1:28 PM
13	2:57 PM	3:42 AM	28	3:03 AM	2:14 PM
14	3:39 PM	4:38 AM	29	4:06 AM	3:05 PM
15	4:24 PM	5:31 AM	30	5:10 AM	4:03 PM

1) Describe one pattern you have learned about the moon rising and setting.

2) Then list one piece of evidence from this data table that supports the pattern you described. Be specific!

3. Moon Phases Follow a Pattern

Fill in these circles to represent each phase of the moon. Shade in the part of the moon that is dark.

Keep this saying in mind: "More light on the right, more moon each night."

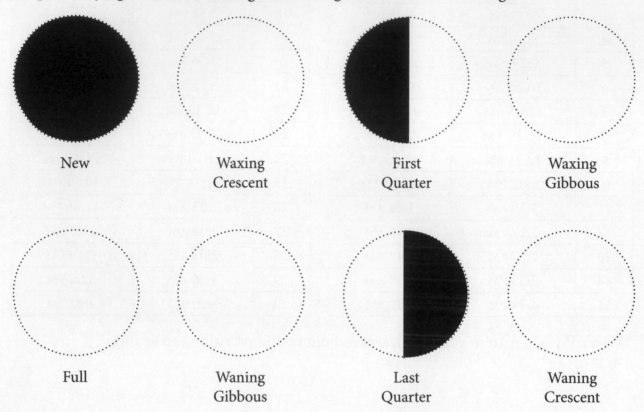

New	Waxing Crescent	First Quarter	Waxing Gibbous

| Full | Waning Gibbous | Last Quarter | Waning Crescent |

4. The Moon's Patterns Are Related

Day	Moonrise	Moonset	
1	5:24 AM	4:28 PM	
2	6:29 AM	5:24 PM	
3	7:33 AM	6:25 PM	
4	8:34 AM	7:30 PM	
5	9:29 AM	8:37 PM	
6	10:20 AM	9:43 PM	
7	11:05 AM.	10:48 PM	
8	11:46 AM	11:50 PM	
9	12:24 PM	12:15 AM	
10	1:02 PM	12:50 AM	
11	1:39 PM	1:48 AM	
12	2:17 PM	2:46 AM	
13	2:57 PM	3:42 AM	
14	3:39 PM	4:38 AM	
15	4:24 PM	5:31 AM	
16	5:12 PM	6:23 AM	
17	6:01 PM	7:12 AM	
18	6:52 PM	7:57 AM	
19	7:44 PM	8:39 AM	
20	8:36 PM	9:18 AM	
21	9:28 PM	9:55 AM	
22	10:20 PM	10:29 AM	
23	11:13 PM	11:03 AM	
24	11:50 PM	11:45 AM	
25	12:07 AM	12:11 PM	
26	1:03 AM	12:48 PM	
27	2:02 AM	1:28 PM	
28	3:03 AM	2:14 PM	
29	4:06 AM	3:05 PM	
30	5:10 AM	4:03 PM	

1) Read each scenario. Then use your Student Text and the data in the table to predict the moon phase.

a) Marcus goes outside on a clear night at 6:45 PM He sees the moon rising in the eastern sky. The next morning he wakes up at 6:30 AM He runs outside to see the moon setting in the west. What moon phase does he see?

b) Sara sees the moon rising in the east when she goes outside for recess at about 1 PM She notices that the moon is in the sky all afternoon and evening. That night, a noise wakes her up at 12 AM midnight. She looks out her window and sees the moon setting in the west. What moon phase does she see?

Day	Moonrise	Moonset
1	5:24 AM	4:28 PM
2	6:29 AM	5:24 PM
3	7:33 AM	6:25 PM
4	8:34 AM	7:30 PM
5	9:29 AM	8:37 PM
6	10:20 AM	9:43 PM
7	11:05 AM	10:48 PM
8	11:46 AM	11:50 PM
9	12:24 PM	12:15 AM
10	1:02 PM	12:50 AM
11	1:39 PM	1:48 AM
12	2:17 PM	2:46 AM
13	2:57 PM	3:42 AM
14	3:39 PM	4:38 AM
15	4:24 PM	5:31 AM
16	5:12 PM	6:23 AM
17	6:01 PM	7:12 AM
18	6:52 PM	7:57 AM
19	7:44 PM	8:39 AM
20	8:36 PM	9:18 AM
21	9:28 PM	9:55 AM
22	10:20 PM	10:29 AM
23	11:13 PM	11:03 AM
24	11:50 PM	11:45 AM
25	12:07 AM	12:11 PM
26	1:03 AM	12:48 PM
27	2:02 AM	1:28 PM
28	3:03 AM	2:14 PM
29	4:06 AM	3:05 PM
30	5:10 AM	4:03 PM

2) Read each scenario. Then use your Student Text and the data in the table to predict the time of day that the moon will rise and set.

a) Jose looks up at the sky. He notices that the moon looks like a crescent "C" shape. The left side of the moon is lit so it must be a waning crescent moon. At what time of day will the moon rise and set?

b) Sheila is totally confused. She is looking for the moon late at night but can't find it! There aren't any clouds, so she thinks it must be a new moon. At what time of day will the moon rise and set?

In this Science Skill Builder, you will observe a moon rise and predict how the moonrise time and moon's phase will change. Then you and a partner will collect data from three moon cycles to see how the pattern of moonrise times and the pattern of the moon's phases are related.

1) Write the name of the moon's phase you are assigned, and fill in the circle to represent the phase. Record the moonrise and moonset times for your phase.

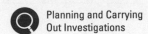
Planning and Carrying Out Investigations

Phase: _____

	Cycle 1	Cycle 2	Cycle 3
Moonrise			
Moonset			

2) Plot data of moonrise times for different moon phases:

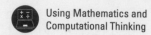
Using Mathematics and
Computational Thinking

- Assign a color for each phase in the graph key.
- Plot moonrise data for your phase in the moonrise times graph.
- Go over the moonrise data together as a class and plot the moonrise times for each phase.

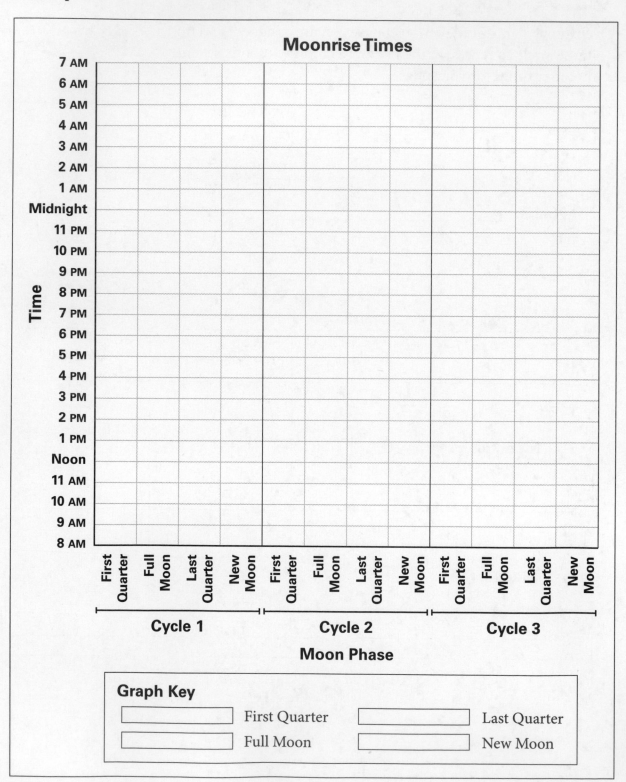

3) Use the same colors as your moonrise graph. Plot data of
moonset times for different moon phases.

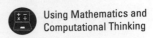

Using Mathematics and
Computational Thinking

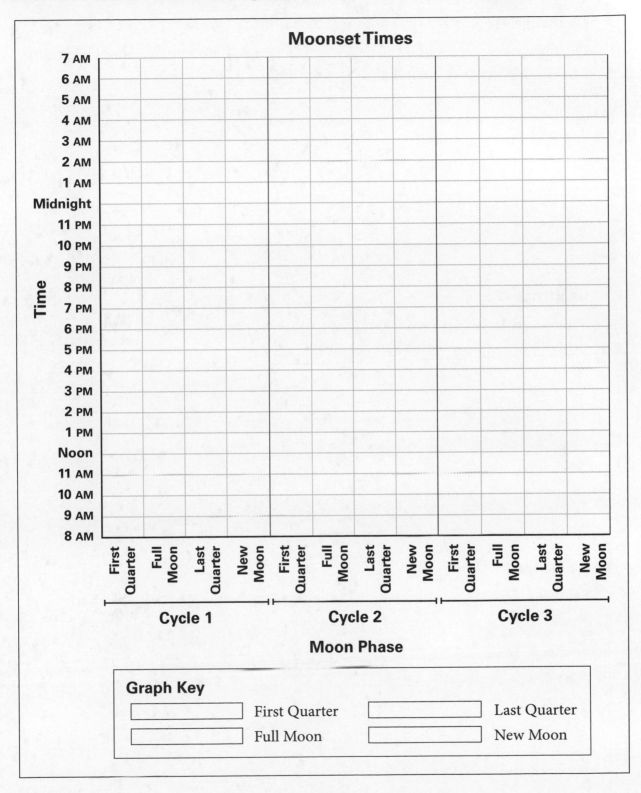

4) Use your graphs to answer these challenge questions.

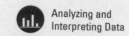
Analyzing and
Interpreting Data

Challenge #1:

During one moon cycle, a full moon sets at around 6:00 AM. At around what time can you predict that the full moon set during the next cycle?

Challenge #2:

Sofia wants to get up around 6:00 AM to observe the moon rise in the morning. Which moon phase would she observe?

Challenge #3:

Ian sees a first quarter moon high in the sky. At what time of day will it set?

Challenge #4:

An astronomer sees a quarter moon rising just after midnight. Is this moon waxing or waning?

Challenge #5:

Karla sees a moon setting at around noon. What phase will the moon's phase be a week later?

Challenge #6:

Greg saw a moon rise some time between 8:00 AM and 5:00 PM. Is it a waxing moon or a waning moon?

Complete the table below by writing the letter of the piece that best fits each space.

Data from a Moon Cycle Investigation

Day 1	Day 8	Day 18	Day 28
New Moon	First Quarter	_____	_____
The moon rises around sunrise. The moon sets around sunset.	_____	_____	The moon rises early in the morning. The moon sets around afternoon.

A) The moon rises around sunset. The moon sets around sunrise.

B) Full

C) The moon rises around noon. The moon sets around midnight.

D) Waning Crescent

Explain how you knew where to place each piece of data in the table. Use the term **pattern** in your answer.

What Tools Do Scientists Use to Observe Space?

Phenomenon: Tools help us see space in greater detail.

What questions do you have about this phenomenon?

After the lesson, use what you learned to explain this phenomenon.

1. Tools Help Scientists See Light from Stars

1) Draw a picture that illustrates the following main idea from the Student Text:

> "Although stars produce a lot of light, most of it is not headed toward Earth. So, only a small amount of a star's light reaches Earth."

2) Why do scientists need to use tools to observe stars?

2. Lenses Refract Light

1) Draw a diagram showing how a lens refracts light. Label the key parts.

2) Explain your diagram using these terms: **bend**, **focus**, **lens**, **light rays**, and **refraction**.

3. Refracting Telescopes

Look at these two refracting telescopes. You could buy the telescope on the left at a store.

The telescope on the right is located in Flagstaff, Arizona at the Lowell Observatory. Mr. Lowell used it in 1896 to look at details on the planet Mars. Mars is even further away from Earth than the moon!

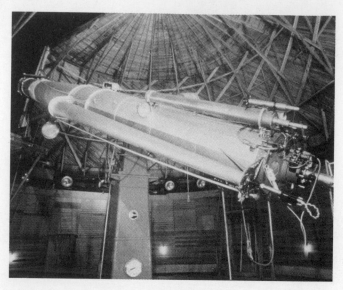

1) Which telescope would be able to collect more light? What is the benefit of being able to collect more light?

2) What are problems with making and using an extremely large refracting telescope?

4. Isaac Newton and Reflecting Telescopes

Suppose you want to explore a dim, distant star. Would you choose a **refracting** telescope or a **reflecting** telescope? Why?

5. Space Telescopes

Carefully observe the picture of the Hubble telescope. Then, use complete sentences to answer each question.

1) What kind of telescope is Hubble?

2) Why is Hubble able to see farther into space than most telescopes on Earth?

3) What are some important discoveries made by Hubble?

6. Radio Telescopes

1) What are two types of light from stars that we cannot see with our eyes (even using lenses)?

2) What are radio telescopes?

3) How do scientists "look" at the images from radio telescopes?

In this Small Group Investigation, you will design and build your own spyglasses using the engineering design process.

1) Clearly define the problem you will solve. List your criteria and constraints.

? Asking Questions and Defining Problems

Criteria:

Constraints:

2) With your group, draw and label a diagram of your design for a spyglass. List the materials you will use, and explain how they will help you solve the problem.

Constructing Explanations and Designing Solutions

Diagram:

Materials:

3) Compare your group's design to the sample design. List the advantages and disadvantages of each. Then decide which design you will build and test.

Constructing Explanations and Designing Solutions

| Our Design | | Sample Design | |
Advantages	Disadvantages	Advantages	Disadvantages

Which design will your group build and test? Why?

4) Build your spyglass according to your chosen design. Then have each group member test it. Read lines on the vision test chart, and have a partner stop you when you make a mistake. Compare how many lines you can read with the spyglass to how many you can read without it.

Planning and Carrying Out Investigations

Group Member					
Number of Lines Without Spyglass					
Number of Lines with First Spyglass Design					
Number of Lines with Second Spyglass Design					

5) Based on what you learned by testing your spyglass, modify the design you originally built to improve it. Draw and label a new diagram of your improved design. Explain the changes you made.

Constructing Explanations and Designing Solutions

Diagram of new design:

Changes:

6) Build your improved design, and then test it in the same way you tested your first design. Record your data in the same data table you used when testing your first design.

Planning and Carrying Out Investigations

Astronomers use telescopes to observe and learn about outer space. But these telescopes are very expensive!

Research answers to the questions below. Use multiple print and digital sources.

• When was the Hubble Telescope launched into space?

• How expensive was Hubble to build?

• What is one discovery of the Hubble Telescope that is not listed in Section 5 of the Student Text?

Then create a public service announcement poster that is either for or against the Hubble Telescope. Your poster must
• have a short, catchy title.
• explain in a short paragraph whether you think the Hubble Telescope was worth the cost or not. Include at least one piece of evidence from your research.
• include a simple drawing of the telescope or one of its discoveries.

Cover and Title Page: NASA/ JPL-Caltech/Univ.of Ariz.

Front Matter

iii: Tristan3D/Alamy **v:** Shaiith/ Shutterstock **vi:** Ethan Daniels/ Shutterstock **vii:** PhotoAlto/ Frederic Cirou/Getty Images **viii:** Stocktrek Images, Inc./ Alamy

Unit 1, Lesson 1

1: Pond5 **3L:** Frans Lanting/ MINT Images/Science Source **3R:** Jerry Sanchez/Dreamstime **5:** Radius Images/Alamy **5:** Gabriel Rif/Alamy **5:** Cultura Creative (RF)/Alamy **5:** OJO Images Ltd/Alamy **5:** Johner Images/Alamy **7:** Thinkstock

Unit 1, Lesson 2

13: Pond5 **16:** Matt Egginton/ Dreamstime **17L:** Karayuschij/ Dreamstime **17R:** Tofuxs/ Dreamstime **17T:** Witold Krasowski/Dreamstime **17B:** Sardorrr/Dreamstime **24:** Andreus/Dreamstime

Unit 1, Lesson 3

25: Pond5 **29L:** iStockphoto **29C:** Russell Watkins/shutterstock **29R:** Photosaurus/ Dreamstime **30:** Frank Bach/ Dreamstime **32T:** Thinkstock

Unit 1, Lesson 4

35: Pond5 **39:** sauletas/shutterstock **40:** Brad Calkins/Dreamstime

Unit 1, Lesson 5

45: Pond5

Unit 1, Lesson 6

55: Pond5 **56T:** Glenn Nagel/ Dreamstime **56B:** Library of Congress **57:** Thinkstock **58:** ASSOCIATED PRESS **59:** William Campbell/Sygma/Corbis **60:** Paula Masterson/Dreamstime **60:** Oksanaphoto/Dreamstime **61:** Michael Thompson/ Dreamstime **63:** Alexey Khromushin/Dreamstime

Unit 1, Lesson 7

65: Pond5 **66TL:** Alvera/ Dreamstime **66TR:** Cholder/ Dreamstime **66BL:** Juliengrondin/Dreamstime **66BR:** Nikolay Dimitrov/Dreamstime **67:** Andreasfischer/Dreamstime **67:** Hsagencia/Dreamstime **67:** Photomo/Dreamstime **67:** Mikhail Markovskiy/Dreamstime **67:** Andrew Orlemann/ Dreamstime **69:** Robert Bohrer/Dreamstime

Unit 1, Lesson 8

73: Pond5 **74TL:** Christian Delbert/Dreamstime **74TR:** Danny Hooks/Dreamstime **74BL:** spirit of america/shutterstock **74BR:** Michael Flippo/Dreamstime **75:** Emjaysea/Dreamstime **76:** Greg Amptman/ Dreamstime **77L:** Keithspaulding/Dreamstime **77R:** Oseland/ Dreamstime **82:** Thinkstock

Unit 2, Lesson 1

83: Pond5 **84:** Thinkstock **86:** Thinkstock **89:** Thinkstock **90T:** Thinkstock **90C:** Thinkstock **90B:** Thinkstock

Unit 2, Lesson 2

97: Pond5 **102T:** Thinkstock

Unit 2, Lesson 3

109: Pond5 **113TL:** Thinkstock **113TR:** Thinkstock **113BL:** Westend61 GmbH/Alamy **113BR:** Thinkstock **116:** Thinkstock

Unit 2, Lesson 4

119: Pond5 **122:** Thinkstock **126:** Thinkstock

Unit 2, Lesson 5

127: Pond5 **128L:** Thinkstock **128C:** Thinkstock **128R:** Thinkstock **129:** Thinkstock

Unit 2, Lesson 6

135: Pond5 **144:** Thinkstock **144:** Thinkstock **144:** Thinkstock **144:** Thinkstock **145:** Thinkstock **146:** Thinkstock

Unit 3, Lesson 1

151: Pond5 **157L:** Danny Smythe/Dreamstime **157LC:** Mario Bonotto/Dreamstime **157R:** Thinkstock **157RC:** Johnfoto/Dreamstime **158:** Gelpi72/Pond5 **159:** Thinkstock **160:** Saap585/Dreamstime

Unit 3, Lesson 2

161: Pond5 **162:** Thinkstock **164T:** Thinkstock **164L:** Thinkstock **164C:** Thinkstock **164R:** Thinkstock **166:** Gustavo Andrade/Dreamstime

Unit 3, Lesson 3

167: Pond5 **170R:** Denis Radovanovic/Dreamstime **171:** Robert Semnic/Dreamstime

Unit 3, Lesson 4

175: Pond5 **178:** Thinkstock **179L:** Kelpfish/Dreamstime **180:** Ondreicka/Dreamstime **180:** Andrew Lambert Photography/Science Source **180:** Valentyn75/Dreamstime **180:** Hanhanpeggy/Dreamstime **180:** Thinkstock **180:** Alexandr Blinov/Dreamstime

181: Alexander Ozerov/Dreamstime **181:** Mario Bonotto/Dreamstime **181:** Sergii Dashkevych/Dreamstime **181:** Sylvain Tavernier/Dreamstime **181:** Leslie Banks/Dreamstime **181:** Viorel Sima/Dreamstime

Unit 3, Lesson 5

183: Pond5 **192T:** Ondreicka/Dreamstime **192C:** Valentyn75/Dreamstime **192B:** Hanhanpeggy/Dreamstime

Unit 3, Lesson 6

193: Pond5 **198L:** Thinkstock **198R:** Thinkstock **201TL:** Thinkstock **201TR:** Thinkstock **201B:** Thinkstock

Unit 3, Lesson 7

203: Pond5 **204:** Thinkstock **205TL:** Thinkstock **205TR:** Thinkstock **205BL:** Thinkstock **205BR:** Thinkstock

Unit 4, Lesson 1

211L: Pond5 **211R:** Pond5 **218T:** Thinkstock **218C:** Thinkstock **218B:** Tihis/Dreamstime

Unit 4, Lesson 2

219: Pond5 **227:** Frank Zullo/Science Source

Unit 4, Lesson 3

229: Pond5

Unit 4, Lesson 4

237: Pond5 **244:** Flat Earth Photos/Fotosearch **246:** Nikhil Gangavane/Dreamstime

Unit 4, Lesson 5

247: Pond5 **249:** Stocktrek Images, Inc./Alamy **250:** Igor Sokalski/Dreamstime **251L:** Larry Landolfi/Photo Researchers, Inc. **251R:** Babak Tafreshi/Science Source **253:** Americanspirit/Dreamstime

Unit 4, Lesson 6

257TL: Dejan Ljamić/Dreamstime **257BL:** Katharina Notarianni/Dreamstime **257R:** Ronald Pickering/Dreamstime **261-262:** Shutterstock

Unit 4, Lesson 7

269: NASA **272L:** Aleksvf/Dreamstime **272R:** JOHN SANFORD/SCIENCE SOURCE **273:** ASA & ESA, Acknowledgement: Gilles Chapdelaine **274:** NASA, ESA, and the Hubble SM4 ERO Team **275L:** Image courtesy of NRAO/AUI **275LC:** Image courtesy of NRAO/AUI **275R:** Image courtesy of NRAO/AUI and Patrick A. Lofy, Photographer **275RC:** Image courtesy of NRAO/AUI